Canine Behavior
A Photo Illustrated Handbook

Barbara Handelman, M.Ed, CDBC

Dedication:

I dedicate this book to my husband, Bob.

With the twirl of a maple seed

You entered my heart.

We nurtured two spirits

They giggled and grew.

With roots in the gardens

Wings carry them far.

Gray hairs accent

Our love as it deepens.

And to Debi Davis.

I cherish your being in my life.

You are my friend, my mentor, and my spiritual sister.

Your voice resonates within me now and forever.

Table of Contents

Section 1:
Acquired Bite Inhibition – Amplitude 1

Section 2:
Anatomy

Section 3:
Anthropomorphism – Butt Sniff

Section 4:
Cache – Displacement Behavior

Section 12:
Lick Intention – Locomotion

Section 13:
Lumpy Whisker Bed – Muzzle Punch

God made the earth, the sky and the water,
the moon and the sun. He made man and
bird and beast. But He didn't make the dog:
He already had one.

– Native American Saying

There was never a king like Solomon
Not since the world began
Yet Solomon talked to a butterfly
As a man would talk to a man.

Rudyard Kipling

Legends speak of the biblical character, King Solomon, who was able to talk the language of animals, which was hidden from all other humans.

Acknowledgments:

Many people helped to weave this book together. I could not have done it without them. I want to especially thank the following individuals:

My human family, Bob, Kali, and Sasha – each of you contributed to this book in your own way. Your patience and faith have meant more to me than words can say.

All the dogs who have enriched my life, especially Beau who is present in my earliest memories, Spoon, Moss, Skye, Spin, Moon, Luca and Pan, for accompanying me through my adult years and teaching me about sheep herding, disability service work, and the often humbling tribulations of agility competition.

My sisters Elly Rubin and Joanne Leonard – you have embraced me with your confidence and vision. I am thankful for all we continue to share as our lives evolve.

Lore Haug and Sue Alexander, my primary editors, I cannot begin to describe your generosity. Your contributions ensured accuracy and clarity within the book. Your patience with my endless questions, frequent frustrations, and moments of panic proved boundless. I cannot imagine having made it through this creative process without your support. Thank you, also to Sophia Yin, who brought fresh eyes to the project in the eleventh hour.

Dee Ganley, you have mentored me with great patience.

Doug Lufkin – I owe you so much. You have seen this project through from its rough-edged beginnings to its polished completion. Your artful touches are everywhere in the book. It has been a rare gift to work so closely with you. Your boundless patience and playfulness lent humor to our work, especially when it seemed we had embarked on a never-ending creative adventure

To Marie Ricketts, thank you for our ever-deepening friendship, and for urging me to abandon the computer and join you for the splendor of our country road walks. You have read through the book's many iterations and offered valued comments and critiques.

Monty Sloan – thank you for your faith in me. I appreciate your trusting that I could do justice to your incredible photographs. Your images give the book power, depth and humor. Most of all, thank you for sharing your wealth of knowledge about our friends, the wolves.

I thank Cindy Arnold, for your careful proof-reading and Robyn Mosher for stepping in to take over the intricate task of creating the index.

Thank you also to veterinary behaviorist, Sophia Yin, who brought fresh eyes to the project in the eleventh hour.

Foreword

Those of us that have been involved in canine related fields for decades remember the paucity of information on canine behavior that was available "back when". Truly, years ago there was no information on dog behavior, only on dog training. We tried to understand, and communicate with, our most intimate animal companion by interpreting their behavior within the framework of human social rules. When this was unsuccessful, we treated dogs as variably colored wolves and found this approach wanting as well – for the simple reason that dogs are not wolves.

We now have a rich collection of resources on canine behavior. We appreciate that dogs are more cognitively and emotionally complex than we originally believed. We recognize that dogs can serve as useful models for some human psychiatric conditions and behavioral disorders. Our increasing knowledge of their similarities to humans in neuroanatomy, neurophysiology, and neurochemistry implies that we should approach our relationship and communication with dogs with more sophistication than we have in the past. Cognitive research in dogs shows us that dogs have, in their way, made special efforts to understand us and our unique relationship with them. It is time that we returned the favor and made concerted efforts to understand their communication with each other and with us.

This beautifully illustrated pictorial guide explores the complexity of our canines and their communicative behaviors. Most importantly, it acknowledges both their similarities to other canids, and their differences. We can use wolf, coyote, fox and jackal behavior to help us understand dogs, as long as we accept that dogs are not wolves, coyotes, foxes or jackals. Dogs have their own selection pressures, both natural and artificial, that have in the past and will continue in the future to shape their phenotype and behavior.

Wolf ethologists, dog trainers, multispecies trainers, psychologists, researchers, and clinical veterinary behaviorists all have contributed to our knowledge pool. For years it seemed as if ethologists, trainers, and clinical behaviorists were studying different species, so diverse at times were their interpretations of dog behavior. Knowledge brings enlightenment and, thankfully, this discord is resolving. Ms. Handelman's book has distinction of being the first reference on dog behavior that truly spans these disciplines and brings together the erudition and wisdom of ethologists, dog trainers, and clinical veterinary behaviorists in a coherent text.

Barbara Handelman has brought us a wonderful gift – a reference that truly celebrates our dogs at their best and worst moments. Even if you are not in search of answers, you will enjoy curling up with this book and taking a journey through the lives of our dogs.

Good reading,

Lore I. Haug, DVM, MS, DACVB, CABC, CPDT
South Texas Veterinary Behavior Services

Keys To Using This Book

- Italics indicate that definitions for the italicized words appear in another section of the book.

- Terminology is introduced in alphabetical order.

- Related behaviors are grouped in categories with section headings.

- Definitions are cross referenced so that related behaviors may be easily found in their own sections.

Vocabulary

Canid (Noun, S): any of a family of (Canidae) of carnivorous animals that include the wolves, jackals, foxes, coyote, and domestic dog (Miriam Webster). (**Canids, Canidae**, pl, adj: **canine**).

Etymology: any of a family (Canidae) of carnivorous animals that includes wolves, jackals, foxes, coyote, and the domestic dog.

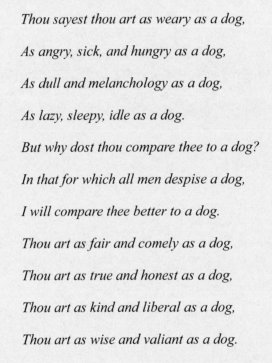

Thou sayest thou art as weary as a dog,

As angry, sick, and hungry as a dog,

As dull and melanchology as a dog,

As lazy, sleepy, idle as a dog.

But why dost thou compare thee to a dog?

In that for which all men despise a dog,

I will compare thee better to a dog.

Thou art as fair and comely as a dog,

Thou art as true and honest as a dog,

Thou art as kind and liberal as a dog,

Thou art as wise and valiant as a dog.

— Sir John Davies

Introduction

The developing field of canine behavior and communication needs a consistent vocabulary with which to describe observed behaviors. This book is offered for the purpose of creating a consistent lexicon of commonly used terminology.

The information required to interpret behavior lies in the environmental contexts in which the behaviors are offered. Distinct communication behaviors rarely appear in isolation; instead, three or more forms of bodily expressions may be present concurrently. The resulting impression is greater than the sum of the component expressive parts.

Not all behavior has communicative intent, but all canine communication emanates from behavior.

Humans can be both angry and sad, or happy and anxious in relation to a single event or interaction. Conflicting emotions exist in canid interactions, just as ambivalence is a component in most human relationships.

Monty Sloan

Wolfgang, a Beta wolf uses many signals to threaten Renki, a lower ranking wolf. Note that Wolfgang, on the left, assumes a tall confident posture, with both his tail and his head raised, ears forward, and piloerector reflex apparent (hackles raised). Renki crouches submissively, as he moves forward, with his tail dramatically tucked between his legs. Renki further expresses his submissive intent with his ears pressed back, and his head slightly lowered. He shows mild piloerector reflex.

To accurately label canid behavior the observer must watch the animal's whole body. Note whether he appears relaxed, tense, stiff, aroused, fearful, aggressive, submissive, or appeasing. Also spot the ways in which elements of more than one feeling state coexist.

Prior to discovering Monty Sloan's Wolf Park photos and the "Wolf Ethogram," (Goodman, et al., 2002), this author had not considered that there might be very close similarities between the communication signals, displays and expressions conveyed by the various canine cousins.

For hundreds of years, humans have genetically manipulated dogs. Dog breeds evolved to fulfill the vanity, utilitarian purpose and companionship needs of humans. One might be drawn to the conclusion that those genetic changes would have caused considerable dilution or alteration of inherited communication behaviors.

> Domestic dogs, in general, no longer depend on submissive displays for their own survival to the extent that their canine cousins do. Dogs rely more on humans to intervene to prevent or interrupt agonistic encounters, and after fights, to heal their wounds. Such wounds occurring in a wild population would most likely lead to death of the injured individuals (Goodwin et al., 1996, p. 302).

The idea that human families and their pet dogs join to form packs that mirror the pack order of wolves became popular among pet dog trainers and owners during the late 1970s and ensuing decades.

The 1978 publication of the book "How To Be Your Dog's Best Friend" by the Monks of New Skete, popularized the notion that wolves use force to dominate each other, as well as establish and maintain pack order. The Monks' premise was based on 1940s studies, supported by limited observations of wolves. Those early studies promulgated substantial misinterpretation of wolf behavior.

Nevertheless, the idea of a force-based hierarchical order among wolves took on the mythic proportion of gospel. Projecting the myth a step farther, the Monks and their followers proclaimed that humans must use force to establish *dominance* over dogs.

In fact, more recent and extensive studies (see Mech, 1999) show that wolves rarely use violence to establish *dominance* or to maintain their status within the pack. During conflicts, the submissive wolf acquiesces and displays *submission* in response to other wolves' dominant social status and posturing. Rank or hierarchy disputes among wolves are usually resolved through *ritualized aggression*, without injury to either the wolf who emerges as the victor or the one who submits.

People who force dogs into a submissive posture behave toward dogs in a manner that neither wolves nor dogs ordinarily behave toward each other. Furthermore, *alpha rolls* are a form of punishment.

Even the Monks of New Skete, in the 2002 revised edition of their book, disavowed their original theories about the appropriateness of 'wolf *alpha roll*s' as a form of discipline in the context of human-dog relationships. They wrote:

These alpha roll interactions include both dominance displays and passive submission. Neither the dogs above nor the wolves to the right use physical force as a tactic in these interactions.

We no longer recommend this technique and strongly discourage its use to our clients. Though it can be argued that it has a natural basis in pack life, in a dog-human context it is potentially very dangerous and can set up the owner for a serious bite in the face (or worse), particularly with a dominant dog. The conditions in which it might be used effectively are simply too risky and demanding for the average dog owner; there are other ways of dealing with problem behavior that are much safer and, in the long run, just as effective.

The American Veterinary Society of Animal Behavior (AVSAB) states the following in its position statement regarding punishment.

... punishment (e.g. choke chains, pinch collars, and electronic collars) should not be used as a first-line or early-use treatment for behavior problems. This is due to the potential adverse effects, which include, but are not limited to: inhibition of learning increased fear-related and aggressive behaviors, and injury to animals and people interacting with animals.

Adverse Effects of Punishment

AVSAB recommends that training should focus on reinforcing desired behaviors, removing the reinforcer for inappropriate behaviors, and addressing the emotional state and environmental conditions driving the undesirable behavior. This approach promotes a better understanding of the pet's behavior and better awareness of how humans may have inadvertently contributed to the development of the undesirable behavior.

Current dog training practices that adhere to the science of *Canine Learning Theory* and the tenets of *Operant Conditioning*, promote positive reward-based training methods, and discourage the use of force-based corrections or other aversives.

Wolves are not dogs and dogs are not wolves. That dogs do share a common language with their canid cousins is a source of great fascination to this author – which hopefully the readers will share. In many instances, photographs of wolves or other canids were chosen to illustrate behavioral terminology for the very fact that the heightened *amplitude* of wolf displays makes the behavioral attributes vivid. Thus, the behaviors may be more easily identified by a novice observer. It is hoped that novice observers will then apply their new knowledge to the more subtle displays offered by domestic dogs.

What is Behavior?

Behavior is the way an animal reacts to or interacts with its immediate environment. Some behaviors are voluntary, while others are involuntary physiological responses to environmental stimuli or stressors. To be considered "behavior," an action must be both observable and measurable.

> "Language is behaviour in as much as it communicates intention, emotion and affects others' behaviours" According to Ken Ramirez, behavior is "any activity of animals or men which is directly observable and where it is possible for two or more observers to agree on what they saw or heard" (Ramirez, 1999, p. 536).

Observing Behavior Without Making Judgments About Intention

To best understand behavior, the observer must distinguish between empirical descriptions such as: tail up, head high, ears erect, body forward in greeting posture; and functional patterns such as: dominance or status-seeking behavior. The observer cannot accurately jump from behavioral descriptions of a single interaction to a conclusion about the canid's intentions.

Dominance seeking is a functional pattern that occurs mostly within established canine social groups. By lumping together the behaviors described above, and calling them "dominance seeking" the observer makes a huge leap. Calling the collective behaviors an "aroused posture" would be more accurate and not dependent on an assumption about intention.

When viewing a display of *fear*, the observer is apt to see the animal's head lower than his body, his ears flattened, and while snarling, the mouth may be partially open with relatively retracted lips. These are empirical descriptions of postures and expressions in a specific context. It would be inaccurate to conclude that a single submissive response signifies the canid's subordinate status within the group's social structure.

Observers can clearly describe a fearful animal. Fearful behavior and subordinate status are not synonymous – neither is confident or aroused behavior synonymous with dominant status.

Empirical behaviors are observable, and can be described in the same terms by anyone witnessing the behavior. Aroused, confident, or fearful behaviors in a single, specific context should not be used to label a dog as having a "dominant" or "submissive" personality type.

Monty Sloan

Three frightened wolves, on the left: tails tucked, ears back, gaze lowered, backs rounded. Their weight is shifted back and movement portrays avoidance and retreat. Piloerection apparent on fearful wolf on the far left and ambivalent wolf who is most forward among the three aggressive wolves on the right. Their aggression is apparent in more upright postures, forward movement, ear positions and forward commissures of the lips.

Barbara Handelman

The English Setter on the left is fearful. She cautiously approaches the stuffed dog. Note: piloerector reflex evident especially over her shoulders and rump. Everything about her posture is angled backwards, away from the object that has caused her fear.

Barbara Handelman

"Dogs are... wonderful. Truly. To know them and be with them is an experience that transcends – a way to understand the joyfulness of living and devotion."

– Gary Paulsen
"Winterdance"

"The wolf is neither man's competitor nor his enemy. He is a fellow creature with whom the earth must be shared."

– L. David Mech

Canine Cast of Characters

Bronte, 3 Year-old male, Airedale, pet dog. Plays well with dogs of all ages and gender.

Bianca, 2 1/2 year old Great Pyrenees, adopted as a stray while pregnent, and Ian, male Poodle, surrendered for adoption at age 5 years, in training as a therapy dog.

Cary, 3 year-old Collie, Assistance Dog, also competes in Rally Obedience and AKC Conformation

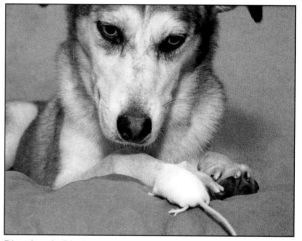

Diaz, Aussie/Husky mixed breed, 3 year-old female pet.
Photo Sabarika

Lear, one-year-old male, Great Pyrenees puppy from Bianca's litter.

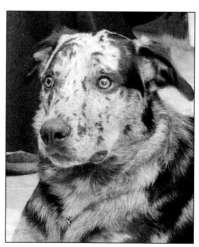

Leo, 9 month-old, male, Aussie Mix, rescued at 4 weeks of age from a parking lot.

Louie, the gentle giant. He was rescued at age 7 months. He is an Anatolian/Great Pyrenees mix.

Luca, 7 year-old, German Shepherd, the author's mobility assistance dog retired at age 5 years.

Moon, the Aussie, now 10 years old, He had a short career as an assistance dog, and a long, successful career as the author's agility dog. He competed in agility with Barbara using a power wheelchair.

Pan, at 10 months-of-age. He is a Smooth Coated Collie and the author's current mobility assistance dog.

Sam, 7 year-old Border Collie, very intense agility dog who also loves to fetch.

Scout, 2 year-old Greyhound, adopted off the race track. Our anatomical model dog.

Wargas, 3 year-old, male Anatolian Shepherd, hearing alert assistance dog.

Wicked, 2 year-old, male Lurcher, aerodynamic, acrobatic comedian.
Photo by Marco De Kloet

Grey Wolf Residents
of the Main Pack at Wolf Park, Indiana

Photos by Monty Sloan

Tristan, born 1998, male, Alpha Grey Wolf.

Kailani, born 2004, the only female wolf in the main pack of Grey Wolves.

Wolfgang, born 2005, male Grey Wolf, litter mate to Woton.

Renki, born 2004, male Grey Wolf .

Woton, born 2005, male Grey Wolf.

Ruedi, born 2004, the Omega male Grey Wolf, littermate to Kailani, Renki and Ayla.

Ayla, female Grey Wolf, born 2004, littermate to Kailani, Renki and Ruedi. Now lives as a singleton, enjoys meeting human visitors to the park.

WOLF PARK is an education and research facility devoted to the study of wolf behavior. Founded by Dr. Erich Klinghammer in 1972, the Park keeps animals in large, semi-natural enclosures for observational research and education. The eighteen wolves, three foxes, two coyotes and fifteen bison housed on the property serve as ambassador animals, educating the public about wolves, their relatives and prey species, and their management in captivity.

Coyotes
Photos by Monty Sloan

Red Foxes

Twister, born 2006, male coyote at Wolf Park.

Basil, male Red Fox, born 1995, White phase, red fox, resident at Wolf Park.
Photo by Barbara Handelman

Willow, born 2006, female coyote at Wolf Park.

Ember, female Red Fox, born 2000, resident at Wolf Park
Photo by Barbara Handelman

Wolf Park is the only known facility, which routinely introduces predators to their natural prey. While our healthy American bison have nothing to fear from the wolves, this is still an unparalleled opportunity to view hunting behavior up close, and watch the bison use their natural defenses to chase away the wolves.

For more information visit:
www.wolfpark.org

Devon, female silver phase Red Fox, in summer coat, born 2000, resident at Wolf Park.
Photo by Monty Sloan

Wolfgang, a Beta wolf uses many signals to threaten Renki, a lower ranking wolf. Note that Wolfgang, on the left, assumes a tall confident posture, with both his tail and his head raised, ears forward, and piloerector reflex apparent (hackles raised). Renki crouches submissively, as he moves forward, with his tail dramatically tucked between his legs. Renki further expresses his submissive intent with his ears pressed back, and his head slightly lowered. He shows mild piloerector reflex.

Section 1:
Acquired Bite Inhibition – Amplitude

Acquired Bite Inhibition (ABI):

(Also see *Bite Inhibition, Metasignals, Ritualized Aggression*)

Acquired Bite Inhibition is a term used by some professionals when assessing the degree of damage caused by a dog's bite to a human or another dog. Assessment of ABI is most relevant when behaviorists and trainers design appropriate rehabilitation programs for dogs with an existing bite history. (Donaldson, 2004, page 21).

Marco De Kloet

Wicked has a firm but harmless grib on another dog's jowls. His bite is clearly inhibited, no wounds will result from this interaction.

Affiliative:

(Also see *Greeting Behaviors, Head Press, Hip Nudge, Rally*)

To join with by choice. When a canid seeks the attention or affection of a human he behaves in an affiliative manner.

Overt indicators of the canid's desire to interact with a human: ears forward or neutral position, soft eyes, perched lightly on person's lap, mouth or lips relaxed, tail in neutral position or carried gayly over the canid's back.

Affiliative behavior also occurs in the context of canid-to-canid greeting behavior, and during interspecies greetings.

"When observing dog interactions, a good predictor of low likelihood of aggression is the presence of signs of affiliation or relaxed friendliness. The absence of these behaviors is glaring and usually a sign of problems to ensue" (Donaldson, 2004, p. 76).

Barbara Handelman

The Collie is expressing her affiliative intent by placing her paws lightly on the person's lap, her ears are neutral and turned outward for listening. Her chin is slightly lowered and turned to the side, and her eyes are soft with gaze averted.

Monty Sloan

The three wolves are rallying to greet a familiar person. Their ears are neutral, eyes soft, lips relaxed. Wolf on far left has front feet perched lightly on person's knee.

While studying and photographing the behavior of domestic dogs, responsible professionals make every effort to diffuse aggression that might otherwise escalate. In the event that a potentially dangerous event erupts – the focus immediately turns to action on behalf of canine and human safety. Images in this section on aggressive behavior were captured only when safety was assured for all who were present. For these reasons, several of the categories in this section do not have photo illustrations.

Aggressive Behavior Classifications

Aggression:

> Aggression may be defined as threats, postures or harmful actions directed towards another individual. Aggressive behavior is a form of communication, where the aggressor is attempting to establish greater social distance between himself and the target of his aggression (Alexander, 2003).

Aggression is any behavior that communicates overt challenge, threat or the intent to do harm to another individual including. but not limited to displays such as growling, posturing or snapping (see *Ritualized Aggressive Behavior*). Shoulder slams can be aggressive, even though they are often silent. All aggressive behavior has the potential to escalate to a dangerous canid-to-canid fight or a serious bite to a human.

> We can now settle for a definition of aggressiveness, bearing in mind that aggressiveness is the potential to show aggressive behavior. Aggressiveness is the drive directed towards the elimination of competition (Abrantes, 2005, p. 44).

Monty Sloan

Wolfgang issues an aggressive warning by pinning Wotan and doing a hard muzzle grab.

Alliance Aggression

(Also see *Proximity Sensitivity*):

Alliance aggression occurs when fearful dogs behave aggressively only if accompanied by their person or other dogs with whom they are allied. Alliance aggression may increase in frequency and intensity if there are frequent incidents when the human speaks soothingly to the fearful dog, while the person and dog hold their ground together.

Barrier Frustration/Aggressive Behavior:

(Also see *Bark Lunge*)

Barrier aggression occurs when a canid is frightened and/or frustrated, and cannot escape or get to the target. His arousal is apt to build into aggressive behavior that results in an attack on another animal or bite to a human.

A barrier can be a crate, kennel, fence, leash or tether that prevents the canid from escaping. Initially the dog might be excited and frustrated that he cannot approach and appropriately greet a strange person or dog. *Fear* of the approaching stranger may also be a player.

When a canid is frightened and/or frustrated, and cannot escape, or get to his target, his arousal is apt to build into aggressive behavior that results in an attack on another animal or a bite to a human.

Barbara Handelman

This dog is extremely aggressive toward diesel engine vehicles only when they pass by his territory. He reacts with barrier aggression.

Barbara Handelman

Crated dog displaying barrier frustration. The dog is growling, her ears are back, and her nose wrinkled in agonistic pucker. Although her lips are not retracted enough to display teeth, her growl was threatening, and her stare was direct and intense.

Marco De Kloet

Dog barks aggressively from behind a fence at passersby. Note: ears back, squinty eyes, head raised, commissure is forward.

Biologically-based Aggressive Behavior:

Aggressive behavior caused by medical condition such as idiopathic epilepsy, Cushing's disease, thyroid disorders, brain tumor, or other diseases or disorders.

Competitive Aggressive Behavior:

All canids compete for resources, including, but not limited to, food, treats, toys, human affection, and sleeping space. In this author's household, the most common stimulus for competitive aggressive behavior occurs when all three dogs want to enter the house through the same door at the same time. Food is the catalyst most likely to spark competitive aggression among housemates (dogs), pack members (wolves), and random canids encountering a single food source.

Defensive Aggressive Behavior:

Some canids might issue distancing signals or *displacement signals* to diffuse the aggressive approach of a person or other canid. When those communications do not influence the aggressor to cease his intrusive actions, a defensive attack toward the aggressor, human or canid, might occur.

Dominance Aggressive Behavior:

(Also see *Dominance*)

Dominance aggression is a misnomer. It is possible for a canid to be both dominant and aggressive, but an aggressive attack does not occur because of dominance. Dominance is a quality of a relationship. It stems from leadership – one animal having or taking control in a situation. Only rarely, is dominance established as a result of aggression – but it can be.

"No normal dog attacks because of dominance" (L.I. Haug, letter to author, February 6, 2007).

People often mistake *agonistic* displays as dominance challenges. Dogs may react when humans fail to correctly identify the dog's expressive displays of *fear*, uncertainty or *submission*.

If the human escalates his own threatening behavior, by leaning over the dog, yelling at or hitting the dog, the dog may feel trapped and respond with escalated *agonistic* displays, warnings and threats. In such a situation it is the human who mistakenly identifies the dog's behavior as 'status seeking'. Sadly, if the situation escalates to the point where the dog bites the human who has threatened him, the dog is blamed and mislabeled as 'dominant aggressive'.

Drug Induced Aggressive Behavior:

Some medication side-effects and reactions to toxic ingestions, can cause aggressive behaviors that are atypical for and inconsistent with the dog's personality and *temperament*.

Fear-Related Aggressive Behavior:

(See *Submissive-Aggressive Behavior*, and *Proximity Sensitivity*)

> Fear aggression has the following necessary condition: aggression that consistently occurs concomitant with behavioral and physiologic signs of fear as identified by withdrawal, passive, and avoidance behaviors associated with the sympathetic nervous system (Merck, 2006, Online).

Group-Related Aggressive Behavior:

Some dogs only behave aggressively when in the company of a group or pack of other dogs.

Idiopathic Aggressive Behavior:

As defined by *The Merck Veterinary Manual*:

> has the following necessary and sufficient condition: Aggression that occurs in an unpredictable, toggle-switch manner in contexts not associated with stimuli noted for any other behavioral Aggression diagnosis or with any underlying causal physical or physiologic condition. This diagnosis must be distinguished from any neurologic condition. Intensive characterization of attendant behaviors is necessary....

> Unpredictability is a function of the quality of observational skills and knowledge. Although idiopathic Aggression may be considered a common problem by clients, once a detailed history is collected it becomes clear that this is a rare diagnosis (Merck, 2006, On-Line).

Intra-Sex Aggressive Behavior:

(See *Bitch Wars*)

Some dogs will only fight with others of their own gender. Males are most likely to fight only to make a point. They will usually stop at *ritualized aggression* rather than injure each other. Bitches are more apt to fight to the point of injuring each other.

Maternal-Protective Behavior:

A female who believes her pups are in danger might attack the person or animal she perceives as the threat.

Pain-Related Aggressive Behavior:

Dogs who are sick, injured or suffer from chronic pain may become irritable due to medical conditions. Assuming they have previously had a stable *temperament*, their lashing out aggressively is likely due to pain or illness, rather than the result of personality or *temperament* changes.

> *"If a dog will not come to you after having looked you in the face, you should go home and examine your conscience."*
>
> *– Woodrow Wilson*

Play Escalation/Predatory Drift:

Dogs should always be monitored while playing with each other. Jaw wrestling, play-fighting, rough and tumble and chase games can evolve from *play* into a true fight in the blink of an eye.

Donaldson (2004, p. 105-106) calls this phenomenon "predatory drift". She adds:

> … Predatory drift is the kicking in of predatory reflexes in an interaction that begins as a social interaction. As opposed to regular predation, which happens predictably when a dog with an identified predatory predisposition is exposed to one of his targets, predatory drift can occur among non-identified dogs who had never been predatory before and may never be again after. It kicks in because of specific contextual triggers. The riskiest triggers are:
>
> • Play or a squabble between two dogs that are extremely different in size –the smaller dog panics, yelps and/or struggles. The simulation of a prey item so close that the roles in the interaction drift from a social scuffle to predator-prey…
>
> • Two or more dogs engaging in intense play, chase or a scuffle with a dog that begins to panic, yelp and/or struggle. Dogs have also been known to attack injured dogs and this effect is also facilitated by the attack unit being two or more dogs as opposed to one.

Play Skill Deficits:

(Also see *Demeanor Shifting*, *Play* and *Metasignals*)

> Sometimes when two dogs are playing, the play becomes too intense and tips over into a fight. The genesis of this can be found in the breakdown, or in severe cases, complete absence of the role reversals (also called demeanor shifting) and constant atmosphere cueing that characterize normal play.
>
> …When this system breaks down it's as though one dog becomes a broken record, repeating the same thing relentlessly and often with increasing intensity. The other dog's attempts to move on to something else or get his playmate to dial it down a notch are ignored. Irritation, self defense and fighting can ensue (Donaldson, 2004, p. 18).

Barbara Handelman

Pan and Bronte, two adolescent male dogs, are regular playmates. In this interaction, Bronte, the Airedale, persistently and repeatedly, albeit playfully, bit Pan's forelegs. Pan emphatically did not like the leg biting. Bronte did not shift his demeanor or alter his behavior, despite Pan's escalated use of metasignals including agonistic pucker, rapid huffing, and intense air snapping. Had humans not intervened, this exchange might have tipped over into a real fight.

Predatory Aggressive Behavior:

(Also see *Predation*)

Predatory Aggressive Behavior may involve attacking other canids, sheep, cats, and other small mammals, even small children. A single dog may engage in predatory aggression, or join forces with other free roaming pet or feral dogs.

> Predatory aggressive behavior is part of a functional system, that includes all behavior directed to the capture and killing of prey animals.
>
> In dogs and wolves, for instance, strategies to attack rabbits, cats, and beavers differ from those directed toward cattle, bison and horses, and these slightly differ from killing sheep and goats. Small children may be treated like prey or like social companions, depending on circumstances (Klinghammer, 1992, p. 4).

According to Lore Haug, aggression is an action, not a motivator of other behaviors.

> Fear, hunger, anger, etc. are motivations. Aggression is just behavior that has an intention to do harm, thus by definition, predation falls into this category although the motivation and the physiology for that type of aggression is very different from all the other forms of aggression.
>
> Domestic dogs show behaviors and motivations that will never show up in wild animals. For example, true predatory aggression is silent. Yet many of our domestic dogs bark, growl and lunge in the act of a predatory sequence because they have a high frustration component added into the behavior by the confines of their environments (fences, leashes, too little exercise, owners yanking on their collars, etc). You are unlikely to see a wolf, or even a feral dog, growl or bark at its dinner before attacking it. It would be unproductive to warn prey that you are about to try to catch it.
>
> During predation, canids may become excited by hunting behavior – this is true of all predatory species. But, the type of affect is much different and involves different parts of the brain than those involved in social aggression. It seems that the recovery time is also much different in that predatory "emotion" ends as soon as the hunting behavior does, whereas this is often not so in social conflict situations.
>
> Canids may growl at prey when it tries to fight back, but the growling in that instance would not be classified as predatory because at that moment there are also defensive (self preservation) motivations at work.
>
> Loose dogs do sometimes vocalize at prey – especially once the dog's presence is known to the prey animal. The barking may in part be due to artificial selection for particular breed traits, and neoteny (L.I. Haug, letter to author, April 6, 2007).

Proximity Sensitivity (Also Called Fear Aggressive Behavior):

Donaldson describes proximity sensitivity as "social shyness that presents in a few different ways".

> 1. Obvious fear and avoidance of other dogs – this is the most easy to spot variation.
>
> 2. Pro-active lunging, barking and snapping displays that cease once the other dog is far enough away
>
> 3. Asocial dogs seemingly disinterested in other dogs until the other dog gets too close or makes social overtures – at this point, threat signals such as growling, snarling, snapping or outright fighting ensue ('she's fine as long as other dogs don't get in her face') (Donaldson, 2004, p. 16).

Punishment-Elicited Aggressive Behavior:

Humans who physically punish a dog (kick, slap whip, throw), do not accept the dog's signals of *submission*, and continue the physical punishment without allowing the dog recourse to escape the punishment – leave the dog little choice other than to bite the human. Humans may misperceive the dog's defensive, punishment-related biting behavior as vengeful, and retaliate by further escalating the punishment.

Redirected Aggressive Behavior:

Occurs when a dog redirects his hostility from a primary target to a secondary target.

Examples:

- A dog might turn her aggressive behavior toward a person restraining her when she is frustrated in her efforts to aggress toward another dog.

- A dog wearing a pinch collar or electronic shock collar, receives a painful correction just after the moment she communicates aggressive intent toward another dog. The dog wearing the correction collar associates the pain with the presence of the other dog. Her aggressive behavior toward the other dog will intensify (redirect), as a result of the painful correction.

Barbara Handelman

Louie (taller dog) is aroused by the school bus, and reacts with barrier aggression.

Bianca also gets excited and aroused by the approaching bus. She redirects her aggression from the primary target (the school bus) toward Louie.

Bianca bites Louie. Louie turns away from the bus, and briefly redirects his aggression toward Bianca – then returns his attention to the bus – the primary target of his aggressive arousal.

Resource Guarding:

Some canids guard such obvious things as food, toys, bones or other treats, and sleeping space. Some will also guard not-so-obvious resources such as proximity to human attention/affection, proximity to exits and entrances to favored rooms, etc.

Moon, the Aussie, is guarding a bone.

Wolf on the left is guarding the resources in the food bags.

Ritualized Aggressive Behavior or Threats:

Threat displays that are shown as communication signals but without the intention of actually doing harm. These threats can escalate into injurious fighting but usually only if they are ignored or the sender has some form of behavioral pathology (Lore Haug, letter to author, November 3, 2006).

Ritualized aggression can be differentiated from fighting behavior – with the intent to do harm – by the presence of *metasignals*. *Metasignals,* in the ritualized aggression context, look like the *feinting* and *parrying* that occur during a human fencing match. During actual fights, when there is clear and immediate intent to do harm, canids use jabbing or direct stabbing motions with their teeth as weapons. Standing on their hind legs is a defensive posture – a position from which they cannot inflict maximum harm.

During ritualized aggression, the observer might see the *predation sequence* or other *fixed action patterns* occur with elements missing or out of order. For example, canids might chase, then stalk, or chase without stalking at all. Ritualized aggression is noisy, with lots of vocalizing including growling, screaming, huffing, etc. All-out battles are relatively quiet, especially among wolves, but between some dogs, as well.

The wolves, left, and dogs, right, are engaged in ritualized aggression. They stand on hind legs, clasping each other around the shoulders. There is much huffing, growling, and dramatic displays of teeth, but no apparent intent to inflict harm.

Social Aggression:

Social aggression often refers to aggression of a canid directed toward a human or another dog.

Submissive-Aggressive Behavior (Also Called Fear Aggressive Behavior, and Submission):

As mentioned above, canids are capable of experiencing multiple feelings simultaneously. In particular, canids can be both submissive and aggressive at the same time.

Some canids initially react to threats by behaving submissively. They display appropriate signs of *active submission* by offering *appeasement* signals or otherwise acquiescing to the threatening postures of the other canid or human.

Some canids might offer signs of *passive submission*, by *rolling* onto their backs and exposing their vulnerable belly or *inguinal area*.

Sometimes, the threatening canid or human ignores or does not accept the offered signs of *submission*. The aggressor may escalate his threats instead. The submissive canid's options become limited to flight, immobility (*freeze*) or fight. If flight is not possible, the canid is likely to resort to the survival mode – bite the human or fight the other canid. The submissive canid resorts to *aggression*, aptly called submissive-aggressive behavior.

Monty Sloan

Notice the very different postures of the three wolves. Wolf (on the right) is standing tall, piloerection apparent, eyes squinting, commissure is short, nose wrinkled in agonistic pucker. Wolf (in the foreground) has rolled onto his back to submit, but apparently his appeasement gestures and submission were not accepted. The wolf's threats have continued. The submissive wolf is becoming aggressive, using his legs to fend off the dominant wolf, warning with wide open mouth, fangs bared, ears back. His head is raised and poised to move forward to defend himself. The wolf in the background is in an actively submissive posture, offering a submissive grin, crouching, tail lowered, ears flattened.

Dog lying down displays submissive-aggression

Head lowered, tail tucked, paw-lift, and moderate crouch combine with an agonistic pucker and hard eyes to create a portrait of a submissive-aggressive threat.

Territorial Aggressive Behavior:

Some canids will defend the familiar territory where they reside (which includes the territory they share with *conspecifics* or humans). Territory can include the entire home, property, car and the human's possessions or be limited to the dog's immediate possessions such as his own bed. Territorial aggressive behavior might also result from the dog's misperception of what belongs to him or his person.

Trained Aggressive Behavior:

Some dogs have been trained to respond aggressively, on command, to particular situations or in relation to specific human behaviors (such as hand signals). For some dog/human partnerships Aggression training is sport; for others, it is a deadly serious military, police or other service career. Trained aggressive behavior may go awry if the training is incomplete or poorly done.

Dog demonstrating – trained aggressive behavior.
Note: full mouth bite and hold.

Agonistic:

In the case of canine interactions "agonistic" is most often used to refer to aggressive behavior but can also include behaviors related to dominance displays, submission, and defensiveness.

According to the University of Wisconsin, primate glossary, agonistic refers to:

A range of fighting or competitive behaviors between members of the same species, including attack, threat, appeasement/conciliation, or retreat/flight; regarding aggressive encounters including offensive attacks as well as defensive fighting.

Agonistic Pucker:

(Also see *Amplitude*):

The technical term for an offensive warning snarl.

During an agonistic pucker, the canid's lips are drawn away from the teeth exposing the incisors and canine teeth; the skin above and to the sides of the nasal plane (nose pad) wrinkles; the corners of the mouth are drawn forward shortening the *commissures*; the tongue may be drawn back in preparation for a bite, or it may protrude to create a combination of an agonistic pucker with a *tongue flick/distancing signal.*

Kevin Peuhkurinen

Irish Wolfhound does an agonistic pucker accompanied by a hard stare. Note that her tongue is retracted, which can suggest a bite is imminent.

Marco De Kloet

Mixed-breed dog does an agonistic pucker with lips lifted, canine and incisor teeth bared, commissure forward, tongue retracted, head tilted upwards, staring intently, whiskers flared forward.

Marco De Kloet

This Black Labrador's agonistic pucker is intense. His lips are short and tense, with the commissures very far forward. There are furrows between his eyes, adding to his hard stare.

Allelomimetic Behavior:

Often combined with *et-epimeletic, investigative* and *agonistic behaviors*, sometimes referred to as "Mirroring".

(Also See *Parallel Walking,* and *Vocalization*)

This behavior is defined as doing what the other animals in a group do, with some degree of mutual stimulation. Puppies first do this at about five weeks of age, when the litter begins to run in a group. This foreshadows running in a pack, one of the outstanding characteristics of dog and wolf behavior. To do so, the animals must maintain contact with each other, primarily through vision, but also through hearing and touch (Scott and Fuller, 1965, p. 74).

Barbara Handelman

A group of dogs all looking in one direction as if on cue.

Any behavior carried out in unison with *conspecifics*. Dogs may bark because they hear neighboring dogs barking. Canids join other canids in *digging* activities to enlarge a sleeping hole, or to relieve boredom. At first glance, the fact that two or more canids are maintaining an identical *gait* or posture might look to be a coincidence.

Monty Sloan

Two wolf puppies howl in unison, perhaps out of loneliness for the rest of the pack, or simply because it feels good to howl – together.

Monty Sloan

Two coyotes mirror each others' posture, head position and tilt of their ears to within a hair of exact replication of each other.

Allogrooming (Also Called Mutual Grooming):
(Also see *Epimeletic Behavior* and *Nibble Groom*)

Some canids will groom each other with gentle fervor. They seem to focus most with their tongues on the other animal's face, but will *nibble groom* any part of another animal's body, just as they would their own. *Nibble grooming* is done exclusively with the comb like, pectinate front teeth, using rapid, open and shut movement of the jaws.

Pectinate originates from Latin word *pectin-pecten* meaning comb; akin to Greek *kten kteis* comb: having narrow parallel projections or divisions suggestive of the teeth of a comb (Merriam Webster OnLine).

Barbara Handelman

Luca, the German Shepard Dog , always had crust on his face from excess tears until Pan, the Collie puppy, took up the daily routine of allogrooming – face washing – for his housemate.

Monty Sloan

These two wolves are engaged in allogrooming. The wolf on the left is nibble grooming, while the other does a gentle muzzle grab.

15

Alpha:

(Also see *Dominance*, and *Dominance Hierarchies*)

The alpha animal in a stable long standing group is the animal who controls the resources – food, water, shelter, space, and sometimes the behavior of subordinates. In dogs, who form loose associations that may shift regularly, determining which dog is alpha at any give time is difficult at best (Sue Alexander, letter to author, July 2007).

In my small group of three male dogs, the dominance hierarchy sometimes appears variable. Luca, the German Shepherd, controls most resources. Luca will vocalize gruffly, and lunge toward the other dogs, if they have a treat or toy he wants. He can also assert himself by positioning himself between a resource and one of the other dogs. Moon, the Aussie, is the older dog who helped raise Luca. Moon challenges Luca frequently and persistently. He will often go back for the last "word" in a squabble, but only after I have separated them. Luca is content to walk away. Pan will turn away from all conflicts. He resorts to whining and waiting for intervention by a human if there is a resource he wants but cannot access because of the physical position (Luca lying between me and Pan). If Pan has a cookie, Luca needs only to move in Pan's direction for Pan to abandon the treat. In seven years, Moon and Luca have never had a "real fight" – not once have they drawn blood or left so much as a scratch on the other. Their altercations are very ritualized and noisy. Luca is always physically on top when they do squabble. Moon is faster and will dive after a treat, but if he's not fast enough to consume the food before Luca gets to it – Luca gets the prize.

Rank is not determined just by competition for one resource. The animals must have similar drives for the resources (e.g. must be in demand by all the animals being tested). Often higher ranked animals "give" resources to others because they do not value the resource highly at that instant in time (Yin, letter to author, December 31, 2007).

Monty Sloan

Dominance posture of standing wolf, passive submission and display of inguinal area by the wolf on her side.

Alpha Roll:

(Correctly called **Submissive Roll**)

(Also see *Defensive Aggression, Dominance,* and *Dominance Hierarchy*)

The submissive canid rolls over of his own accord – deferring to the other animal's social status. Humans who force dogs to roll onto their backs or side are not replicating canid behavior and they risk receiving a defensive bite

Lynn Crook

Puppy rolls over in deference to the adult dog's dominant posture and attitude
(standing tall, tail head high, slight agonistic pucker, direct stare)

Amplitude:

The intensity, duration, and frequency of a specific behavior.

Wolves and dogs display many of the same communication behaviors. Wolves generally express themselves with greater amplitude than dogs. Wolf behavior has the appearance of an exaggerated version of dog behavior.

Barbara Handelman

Dog's tongue flick accompanied by whale eye, flared whiskers, nose wrinkled preparatory for agonistic pucker.

Monty Sloan

Wolf with agonistic pucker and tongue extended.

17

Weimaraner is running joyfully, using rocking horse style gait.
Her relaxed ears look like wings, perhaps she'll take flight.
Photo by Marco De Kloet

Section 2: Anatomy

No information in this section or any other section of this book should substitute for medical or behavioral consultation with a licensed veterinarian or certified canine behaviorist. Changes in an animal's behavior may be symptomatic of medical problems for which there are no apparent physical signs or symptoms.

Whether simply living with dogs, or training them for sports or working careers, handlers need knowledge of canine physical structure. Pain or illness can cause or exacerbate behavioral problems in dogs. Dogs who display growling or snapping that is uncharacteristic of their usual personality might be in pain; an eager or willing dog who becomes apathetic, may be ill.

Awareness of basic canine anatomy may enable both pet owners and professionals to supply accurate information about physical symptoms to the veterinarian.

Example:

Luca enthusiastically began agility training as a young dog. He did not jump anything higher than his hocks (4 inches) or do repetitive weaving until all his growth plates (epitheses of the long bones) had closed. Luca usually approached agility with his characteristic gangbusters' attitude.

For months at a time, he completed sequences of agility obstacles with enthusiasm, speed, and grace. Then, seemingly out of the blue, he avoided jumps, or left the agility course to follow a squirrel's trail with his nose. He looked healthy and sound. His change of attitude appeared behavioral in origin. There were no obvious changes in his gait – until two or three days later, when he woke up profoundly lame.

Radiographs and repeated visits with a veterinary orthopedic specialist determined that Luca had Panosteitis*, commonly known as wandering lameness. Panosteitis is a recurrent problem of the long bones, common to physically immature, large-breed dogs, especially German Shepherds. For Luca, short periods of painful lameness, repeatedly interrupted months-long stretches of pain-free activity.

Luca is not unique. For many dogs, the first signs of a medical problem manifest as changes in behavior. It is therefore extremely important for pet owners, professional trainers and canine behaviorists to consider medical causes for sharp or subtle shifts in dogs' behavioral habits, mood, or willingness to perform physical activities. Always rule out medical causes first. Refer the dog to a veterinarian for consultation and appropriate medical testing, before embarking on training or management programs to rehabilitate a behavior problem – especially when the aberrant behavior is new or significantly different than the norm for that particular dog.

* The exact cause of Panosteitis is unknown. It is thought to have a genetic component. It is most common in certain breeds, and more specifically within related lines within those breeds.

The information included in this section is intended as a limited overview of canine anatomy – to offer those who live and work with dogs, a general knowledge of canine anatomy relevant to behavioral activity, and emotional displays. Under no circumstances should the included information substitute for medical diagnostic tests or treatment. The author and publisher assume no liability for injury to you or your pet incurred by following these descriptions.

The Organ Systems:

Adapted from the University of Washington Veterinary College's "Anatomy for the Pet Owner" website

1. **The cardiovascular system** includes the heart and blood vessels. The cardiovascular system performs the function of pumping and carrying blood to the rest of the body. The blood contains nutrients and oxygen to provide energy to allow the cells of the body to perform work.

2. **The lymphatic system** includes the lymph nodes and lymph vessels. The lymphatic system is part of the immune system that helps the body fight off disease. The lymphatic system also works with the cardiovascular system to return fluids that escape from the blood vessels back into the blood stream.

3. **The digestive system** includes the mouth, teeth, salivary glands, esophagus, stomach, intestine, pancreas, liver and gall bladder. The digestive system absorbs and digests food and eliminates solid wastes from the body.

4. **The integumentary system** is the skin and fur that cover the animal's body. The skin protects the underlying organs. The fur helps insulate against heat loss. Dogs do not sweat through their skin. They only sweat from their footpads and nose. Dogs pant as a way of cooling their bodies. Panting is a function of the respiratory system.

5. **The musculoskeletal system** includes all the muscles, bones and joints.

6. **The respiratory system** includes the mouth, nose, trachea, lungs and smaller airways (bronchi and bronchioles). The respiratory system is responsible for taking in oxygen and eliminating waste gases like carbon dioxide. Panting is a function of the respiratory system – panting plays an important role in regulation of body temperature. Panting, drooling and evaporation help with cooling the body – also causing loss of fluids from the body.

7. **The urogenital system** includes the kidneys, ureters, urinary bladder, urethra and the genital organs of both sexes. The urinary system is responsible for removing waste products from blood and eliminating them as urine. The genital organs are involved in reproduction.

8. **The nervous system** includes the brain, spinal cord and all the nerves that communicate between tissues and the brain and spinal cord.

9. **The endocrine system** includes many glands and organs: the thyroid and parathyroid glands, adrenal glands, ovaries, and pancreas, among others, are part of the endocrine system. Hormones are chemical substances that act like messengers in the body. Hormones travel through the blood stream to other parts of the body where they trigger specific functions in the body (e.g. adrenaline is produced by the adrenal gland; insulin is produced in the pancreas; estrogen and progesterone are produced in the ovaries).

10. **The organs of special senses** (eyes, tongue – taste buds, nose, and ears) allow the animal to interact with its environment – through sight, taste, smell and hearing.

11. **The hematopoietic system** includes the bone marrow which is located inside the bones. Three types of blood cells are made in the bone marrow: white blood cells that fight infection, red blood cells that carry oxygen and platelets that are part of the blood clotting process.

www.vetmed.wsu.edu/ClientED/anatomy/#systems

Since dogs have always been present in people's lives, both very rich people and very poor people, they go in tandem with the history of the world. And if you focus on them, you get a mirror of what is important.

– Robert Rosenblum

And when, on the still cold nights, he pointed his nose at a star and howled long and wolflike, it was his ancestors, dead and dust, pointing nose at star and howling down through the centuries and through him.

– Jack London

To a dog, the whole world is a smell.

– Anonymous

The Brain:

The dog's brain synthesizes, interprets, and acts on all the information it receives from the senses. Although the brain of an average dog accounts for less than half a per cent of its body weight, it needs a great deal of nourishment to function properly and receives over 20 per cent of the blood pumped out by the heart. Brain activity is, in part, predetermined by the "fixed wiring," as determined by the dog's genes.

Just as human brains are pre-wired to learn language, the dog's brain is pre-wired to learn to interpret scent, and a large part of the brain is devoted to this process. It is also able to interpret information from the other senses – touch, taste, hearing, and sight (www.avalanche.org/~doghouse).

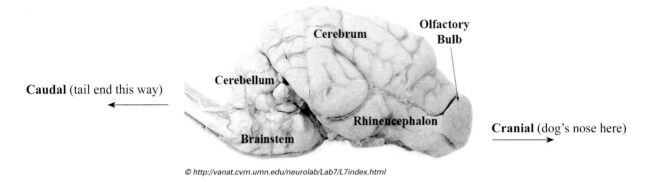

© http://vanat.cvm.umn.edu/neurolab/Lab7/L7index.html

The cerebrum controls learning, emotions and behavior. Gross motor control happens in the motor cortex of the cerebrum. The cerebellum is for fine motor control; it aids in controlling muscles and the coordination of muscles moving in concert with other muscles.

The amygdala controls fear-related behavior. It controls the formation of emotional memory, especially those that are fear-related. It is also important in generation of fear conditioning.

The hippocampus is necessary for the formation of new long term memory, and spatial memory.

The structures of the limbic system collectively generate strong emotional responses, to promote behavioral actions or reactions particularly related to defense and procreation. Much of the rhinencephalon (nose brain) is involved with emotion since self preservation and species preservation were early phylogenetic requirements for survival (Fletcher).

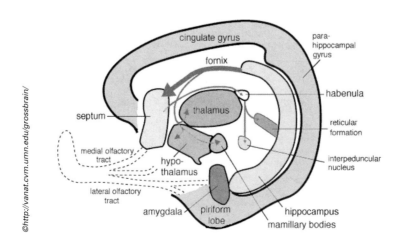

Scent Perception:

The average dog has 200 million scent receptors in its nasal folds compared to a human's 5 million.

The dog also has a vomeronasal organ above the roof of the mouth. It is thought that the vomeronasal organ plays some role in capturing pheromones (sex scent) and transferring it to the brain. Pheromones are chemicals secreted by animals into the environment that provide a communicative function or have an effect on another animal. The vomeronasal organ has been very well studied in ungulates (sheep, cattle, and goats) but but the extent of its functionality in canids is undergoing further research.

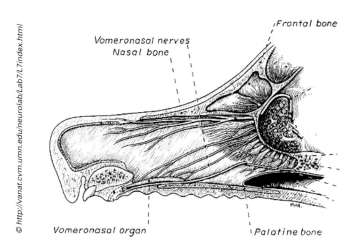

Mammalian vomeronasal sensory neurons detect specific chemicals, some of which may act as chemical-communication signals (pheromones) from other individuals of the same species, and trigger the generation of electrical impulses that carry the information to the brain. The vomeronasal organ is not the exclusive chemosensory organ capable of detecting pheromones. There are some examples where the main olfactory system mediates pheromone communication (Meredith).

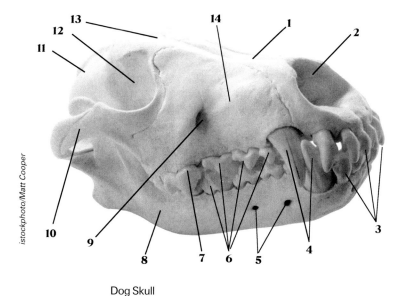

1. Nasal Bone
2. Nasal Aperture
3. Incisors (Pectinate Teeth)
4. Canine Teeth
5. Mental Foramen
6. Premolars
7. Carnassial Tooth
8. Mandible
9. Infraorbital Foramen
10. Zygomatic Arch
11. Parietal Bone
12. Orbital Socket
13. Frontal Bone
14. Maxilla

Dog Skull

Facial Anatomy

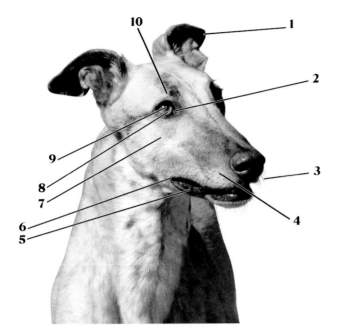

Scout Relaxed Face

1. Pinna
2. Nictating Membrane (3rd Eyelid)
3. Vibrissae (Whiskers)
4. Whisker Bed
5. Relaxed Lower Lip
6. Commissure of Lips
7. Cheekbone
8. Iris
9. Pupil
10. Eyebrow

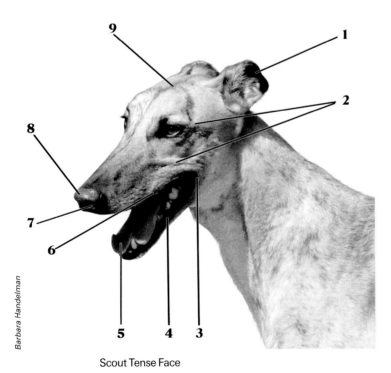

Scout Tense Face

1. Pinna
2. Muscle Tension Ridges
3. Commissure of the Lips
4. Tense Lower Lip
5. Tongue
6. Tense Upper Lip
7. Nares (Nostril)
8. Nasal Planum
9. Skin Taut Over Frontal Bone

Barbara Handelman

External Anatomy

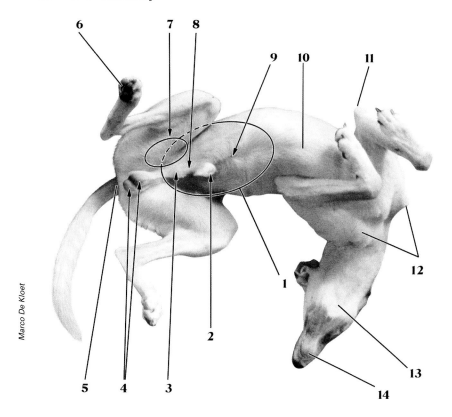

Marco De Kloet

1. Abdomen
2. Opening of Prepuce
3. Bulbus Glandis
4. Scrotum & Testicles
5. Perineum
6. Paw Pads
7. Inguinal Region
8. Prepuce/Penis
9. Umbilicus
10. Sternum
11. Elbow
12. Point of Shoulders
13. Throat
14. Chin

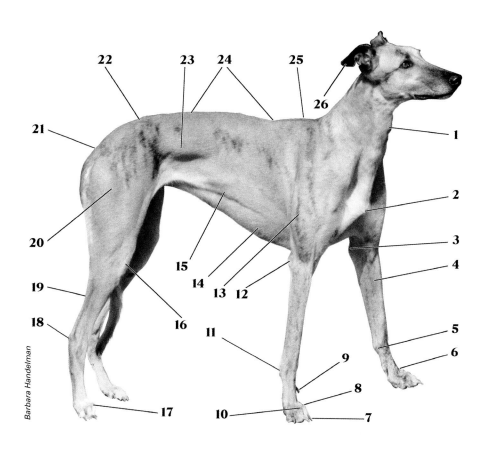

Barbara Handelman

1. Ventral Neck
2. Sternum
3. Elbow (Cubitus)
4. Foreleg (Antebrachium)
5. Carpus
6. Pastern (Metacarpus)
7. Toenail
8. Toe
9. Dewclaw
10. Toes
11. Carpal Pad
12. Elbow (Cubitus)
13. Upper Arm (Brachium)
14. Brisket
15. Flank
16. Knee (Stifle)
17. Toe
18. Hock (Tarsus)
19. Gaskin Crus
20. Thigh
21. Tail Bone
22. Croup
23. Loin
24. Back (Topline)
25. Withers
26. Pinna

Skeletal System

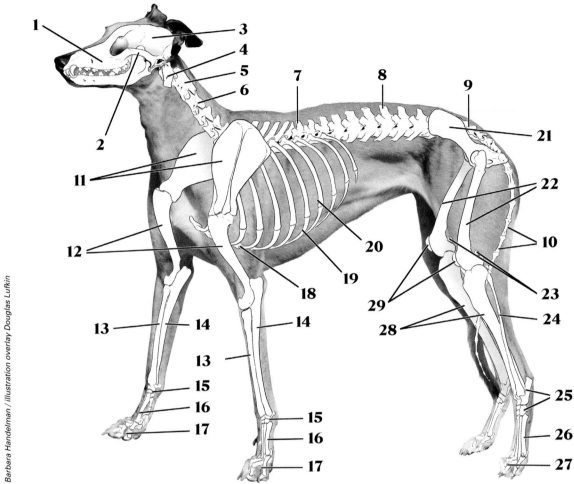

Barbara Handelman / Illustration overlay Douglas Lufkin

1. Maxilla
2. Zygomatic Arch
3. Parietal Bone
4. Atlas
5. Axis
6. Cervical Vertebra
7. Thoracic Vertebra
8. Lumbar Vertebra
9. Sacrum
10. Caudal Vertebra
11. Scapula
12. Humerus
13. Radius
14. Ulna
15. Carpal Bones
16. Metacarpal Bones
17. Bones of Digits (Phalanges)
18. Sternum
19. Costal Cartilages
20. Costa (Rib)
21. Ilium of Pelvis
22. Femur
23. Sesamoid Bones of Gastrocnemius Muscle
24. Fibula
25. Tarsal Bones
26. Metatarsal Bones
27. Bones of Digits (Phalanges)
28. Tibia
29. Patella

Internal Organs

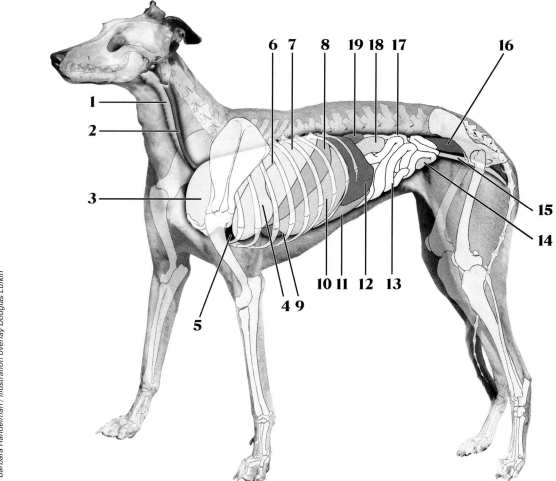

Barbara Handelman / illustration overlay Douglas Lufkin

1. Trachea
2. Esophagus
3. Cranial part of cranial lobe of left lung
4. Caudal part of cranial lobe of left lung
5. Heart
6. Diaphragmatic Cupula (projected)
7. Caudal lobe of left lung
8. Costal part of diaphragm
9. Liver

10. Stomach
11. Greater Ogmentum
12. Spleen
13. Jejunum
14. Urinary bladder (projected)
15. Urethra
16. Rectum
17. Left horn of uterus
18. Descending colon
19. Left kidney

Ear Positions

Airplane Ears:

When dogs' ears are out to the sides of their heads, they are usually in a state of conflict, experiencing more than one set of feelings, without having made a decision how to react. For some dogs, ears out to the side may be their natural, relaxed state.

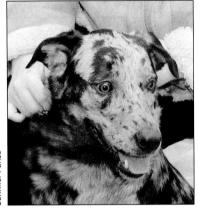

Leo is staring at an approaching stranger. He appears uncertain whether to greet or warn the person.

Pan dislikes having his nails trimmed. His agonistic pucker suggests a serious threat, his airplane ears say he's not sure.

This coyote is displaying airplane ears. Remember, coyote ears usually stand at full prick. He is also doing a tongue flick. Together these signals suggest a conflict of feelings about what he is approaching.

Wicked, the Lurcher, is watching something intently, perhaps someone is about to throw a ball. For Wicked, this is an erect – alert -ear position.

Wicked's airplane ears from the back.

28

Ears Erect or Angled Forward:

Dogs whose ears are forward convey alertness and confidence.

Luca's absolute self-confidence shows in his fully pricked ears.

Ears Back – Appeasement:

Ears back but not flattened convey *appeasement*.

The brown dog in the center has his ears back while doing a head turn displacement behavior. The black and white dog is doing a lip lick, with his face tilted up and his ears back as appeasement displays.

Wicked's Varied Ears Back Positions:

Wicked, the Lurcher, has ears back in varying degrees, dependent on his state of arousal. In the top photo he is playing. Note the open mouths, long lips, commissures well back on both dogs. Wicked is also doing a head turn. This is definitely played. Although their ears are back, both dogs' ears are relatively relaxed.

The aggression in this photo is still ritualized, but could tip over into a real fight. Both dogs are showing whale eye; their lips are shorter, commissures farther toward the front. Only Wicked's front teeth are visible. Wicked's ears are flattened back.

Wicked's ears are pressed back. He is issuing a warning to the other dog.

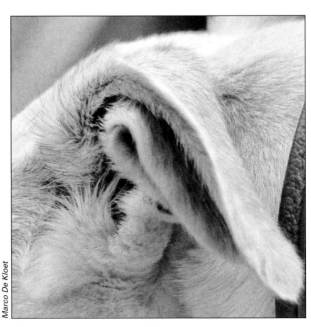

Wicked's ear is back but not flattened.

Ears Semi-Erect, Turned Outward Towards Sound:

The dog is alert and listening. Note that ears can move independently of each other, in order to optimize sound localization.

Ears Flattened Back:

Dogs who are frightened may flatten their ears against the sides of their heads. Ears that are flattened may also suggest an *agonistic response* to a perceived threat.

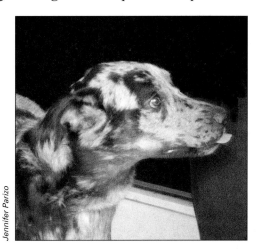

Jennifer Parizo

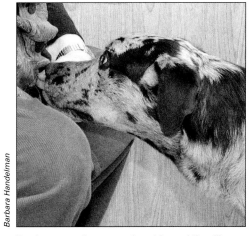

Barbara Handelman

Dog's ears are in a neutral position, while still tense.

Pinch Ear:

Pinch ear is only visible in floppy eared dogs – Labs, Goldens, Hounds, etc. They turn the ear parallel to the side of the face (not forward or back) and pull it toward the skull. Pinch ears occur during times when the dog is extremely stressed or fearful.

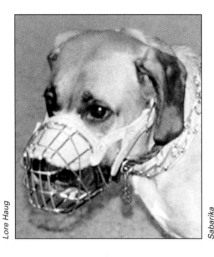

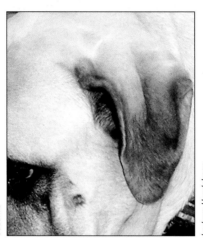

Louie shown here for comparison with the floppy eared dogs with Pinch Ear. Louie has floppy ears that are very relaxed in this photo.

Seal Ears:

"Ears pressed so far back they virtually disappear" (Goodman, et al, 2002).

Wolf with seal ears, in this display of appeasement tinged with submission and fear.

Relaxed Ears:

Each of the photos on this page portray Lurchers with ears in relaxed positions.

Wicked in a playful leap, relaxed ears flopping forward.

In this photo, Wicked's ears are each facing different ways, allowing him to tune in to sounds of interest to him, coming from different directions.

Anna has ears that are alert but relaxed. Although there is a fold in her ear, this is not a pinch ear. Her open mouth and long relaxed lips say she's not frightened or stressed. And her ear is not flattened to the side of her head.

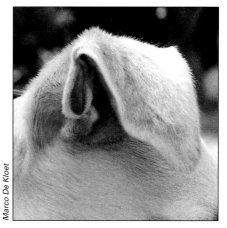

Wicked's ear in a relaxed alert moment.

This ear is angled back for listening but is not pressed or flattened back. This, too, is a relaxed position.

33

Eyes

Eyes express many moods; observed carefully, they can convey feelings as they change from moment to moment.

Dilating Eyes:

"Dogs' eyes dilate from low light and from any situation that triggers sympathetic stimulation, whether it be eustress or distress" (L.I. Haug, letter to author, August 15, 2007).

Sympathetic stimulation refers to stimulation of the sympathetic nervous system, which controls any activity of the body, which is involuntarily (i.e., reflexive), and happens in an automatic manner without conscious control.

Jennifer Parizo

Leo's eyes are almost fully dilated despite ambient light conditions. He is very stressed. Also note whale eye.

Hard Eyes:

When a dog does a "hard eyed stare," his pupils contract. His eyes will be partially open and his brow wrinkled, as if he were scowling. An *agonistic pucker* and other signs of tension building toward a threat, may accompany hard eyes.

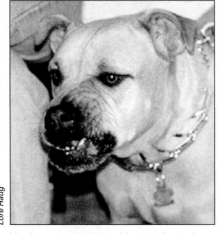

Lore Haug

Hard eyes are squinty with some furrowing of the area between the eyes. Dog is also doing a serious agonistic pucker with short lips and commissure well forward.

Nancy Lyon

This working dog was concentrating intently on her search and rescue mission. Her hard eyes, obvious facial tension ridges, and tongue flick express her indignation at being interrupted for this photo opportunity.

Soft Eyes:

(Also see *Displacement Signals*)

Eyes partially closed as if the dog is squinting slightly; all other postural, facial expressions, and neutral ear position are signals that she is relaxed and non-threatening.

Barbara Handelman

The softness of the German Shepherd Dog's eyes is evident in the softness of her slight squint, and the general relaxation of all other facial features. Her lips are long and the commissure is well back. Her ears are neutral and relaxed as well.

Whale Eye (Also Called Eye Flash):

Whale eye occurs when dogs are stressed or threatening. The skin over the top of their head is so taut that it stretches the eyelids away from the eye, exposing part of the whites of the dog's eye.

The German Shepherd Dog in the lead looks back over his shoulder at his pursuer. His eyes are turned so hard in the other dog's direction that the whites in the corner of his eyes, are exposed.

This young dog is very stressed. He is showing whale eye in both eyes due to the tautness of the skin over his skull.

These jaw sparring dogs are both showing whale eye.

The whites of the eyes may be visible at times when a dog is not stressed, threatened or threatening. A dog who is trying to see something in the extreme range of his peripheral vision will appear to have whale eye because that is what happens, anatomically when the eyes are turned to an extreme position. For example, if a person restricts the movement of a dog's head with one hand while holding a treat out to her side with the other hand, the dog will move his eyes to the limit of their range, and thus display the whites of his eyes, with no stress, or other emotional state contributing.

Lips

(Also see *Commissures*)

Lips speak volumes viewed in context. The changes in the position of a dog's lips convey many subtle and other more dramatic expressions of emotion.

Examples:

- Short Tense Lips, Mouth Closed

- Short Lips Mouth Partially Open, Front Teeth Visible

- Long Lips Forming "C" Shape (Also see Gape), Mouth Wide-open, Teeth Visible, Including Molars

Tension

Agonistic pucker

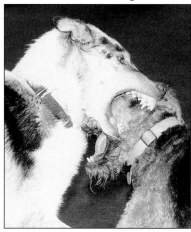
Aggressive warning display

The dog's lips in the two photos below appear similar. The dog on the left is stress panting and drooling, while the dog on the right's tongue is relaxed and lolling. One has to assess all the expressive and anatomical signs to discern the difference.

- Long Lips Tense (see Stress Indicators), Mouth Open

- Long Lips Mouth Open

Tension may include stress panting and drooling

Dog is alert to activity around him but not tense or aroused.

Tail Positions

- Tail Level with the Topline of the Back

This dog's tail is in a natural relaxed position.

- Tail Raised Above the Back

Same dog as the one above. His raised tail suggests play arousal.

- Tail Raised High Over Topline of Back

Sabarika

The dog's raised tail combines with his ears back position and stiff legs to portray signs of tension.

- Tail Raised, Curling Above the Topline

Sabarika

For this Husky, the raised, loosely curled tail is his natural, relaxed tail carriage. If he were aroused his tail would rise higher over his back and curl more tightly.

- Tail Lowered Below Topline

Sabarika

This is the same Husky pictured above. For a husky whose natural tail carriage is high and curled over his back, a lowered tail is a significant contrast. In order to understand the relevance of the posture of a single body part, such as a lowered tail, the observer needs to know what is the "normal" relaxed tail position for that dog.

- Tail Below the Topline of the Back

Natural relaxed tail carriage.

- Tip of Tail Raised Slightly

Ears forward, this dog is alert and excited.

- Tail Tucked Between Hind Legs

Fear or moderate to severe stress. Doberman's docked tail is clamped over anus; she is fearful.
The dog on the right has tail in neutral position, and has slight piloerection; she is uncertain.

- Tail Tucked

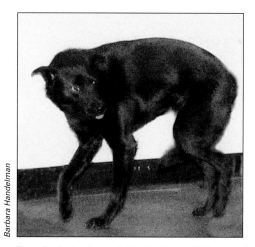

Barbara Handelman

Fear display includes: tail tucked, paw-lift, tongue flick, whale eye, ears back. Moments later, this dog did a fear aggressive lunge and snap at the playful dogs who were not respecting the signals that she wanted to be left alone.

Tail "Flagging"/Averted (See *Reproductive Behavior)*

Monty Sloan

Courting phase of reproduction. Female's tail is averted indicating readiness to mate.

Tail Raised Straight Up

Sabarika

This dog is aroused. Her play face, straight top line, relaxed ears combine with her raised tail to make clear that her playful intentions. A tail raised straight upward, might also suggest confidence, territorial arousal or other emotional states that could lead to aggression.

Border Collie:

A dog's tail position changes with activity and attitude. Different breeds have different natural, relaxed, tail positions. Individuals within a breed may display slight variations of the "norm" for their breed. It is interesting to note that Border Collies often carry their tails over their backs when playing, but almost never do while working sheep. A Border Collie engaged in herding uses his tail as if it were a boat's keel to assist with balance.

- Natural tail carriage – level with his topline, slight curl at the end.

To distinguish between the tail position in this photo and the one below, context and concurrent behaviors are essential to interpretation. Here, Sam has a toy in his mouth and is eyeing the person with whom he is interacting.

- Border Collie's tail raised above topline – play arousal.

- Border Collie's naturally level tail, raised high over back and tightly curled – extremely aggravated arousal evoked by the Collie's relentless sexual pursuit.

Anatolian Shepherd:

A dog's tail position changes with activity and attitude.

- Alert and playful tail slightly raised above topline.

- Tail relaxed. It is waving like a flag in a gentle breeze, with no sign of tension or arousal.

- Tail lowered due to extreme stress – note arched back and *yawn*, also signs of stress.

- Tail lowered – extreme stress – note *sweaty paw prints*. Louie's tail is lowered. In his case this tail posture means that he is extremely stressed. Note the similarity to the Golden's tail on page 40. The comparison makes clear how important it is to know what is normal for the breed and for the individual, before drawing conclusions about the meaning conveyed by a single body part.

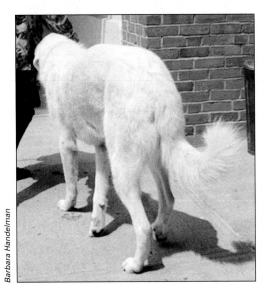

Barbara Handelman

- Tail tightly curved above topline – (Also see *Standing Tall*). For Louie, the tail raised above his top line, combines with his arched neck and stiff straight legs to convey tension and irritation with the Cary the Collie who is doing a muzzle punch.

Barbara Handelman

Golden Retrievals

Fetch? Balls and sticks capture my attention
Seconds at a time. Catch? I don't think so.
Bunny, tumbling leaf, a squirrel who's – oh
Joy – actually scared. Sniff the wind, then

I'm off again: muck, pond, ditch, residue
Of any thrillingly dead thing. And you?
Either you're sunk in the past, half our walk,
Thinking of what you can never bring back.

Or else your're off in some fog concerning
– tomorrow, is that what you call it? My work:
to unsnare time's warp (and woff!), retrieving,
my haze-headed friend, you. This shining bark,

A Zen master's bronzy gong, calls you here,
entirely, now: bow-wow, bow-wow, bow-wow.
                                    – Mark Doty

Appeasement behavior displayed by wolf on the left, who is "licking up" to the wolf on the right – notice her squinty eyes.

Photo by Monty Sloan

Section 3:
Anthropomorphism – Butt Sniff

Anthropomorphism:

Attributing human characteristics, qualities, feelings or attitudes to non-human beings such as dogs, cats, deities, toys, machines, etc. Anthropomorphism becomes problematic when people attribute human motivations to canid behavior or misbehavior. "Owners" often ascribe human motives such deceit, spite, or status-seeking to dogs and then mete out inappropriate punishment based on misinterpretation of the dog's behavior. Pets in general – dogs in particular – become family members with whom humans form intense emotional bonds similar to or taking the place of attachment to human children.

Many researchers also recognize that we must be anthropomorphic (attribute human traits to animals) when we discuss animal emotions, but that if we do it carefully, we can still give due consideration to the animals' points of view. No matter what we call it, researchers agree that animals and humans share many traits, including emotions. Thus, we're not inserting something human into animals; rather, we're identifying commonalities and then using human language to communicate what we observe. Being anthropomorphic is doing what's natural and necessary to understand animal emotions (Bekoff, 2007, p. 50).

Photo by Barbara Handelman, morphing by Douglas Lufkin

Many people treat their dogs as if they were children in fur suits. Anthropomorphism can distract people from understanding canine behavior and how dogs learn.

Appeasement or Pacifying Behaviors:

(Also see *Obnoxious Submission*)

Canids offer appeasement behaviors, also called pacifying behaviors, to suppress *aggressive behavior* that might happen. In contrast, submissive behavior serves to turn off aggression already happening.

Appeasement behaviors are often associated with friendly greetings. The dog who lacks confidence might also offer pacifying behaviors to acknowledge his own social inferiority, or announce his *fear*.

"The differences between pacifying, friendly, fearful or submissive behaviour ar,e generally, small and quantitative" (Abrantes, 1997, p. 184).

Examples: *Pawing*, muzzle-nudge, twist movement, puppy licking, lowered body posture (groveling, wiggly approach), ears back, *submissive grin*, tail and hindquarters wagging.

The wolf in the foreground offers several appeasement behaviors including a tongue flick, pawing, and inguinal display. There is no obvious threat issuing from the standing wolf, but the appeasing wolf, may be reading threatening signals the observer cannot see.

Appeasement signals represent a lack of confidence and serve to avoid hostility. They are a non-aggressive means of achieving escape or prevention of hostile/aversive treatment. Appeasement signals are commonly classified as "distance decreasing" signals, but they are rightly categorized as agonistic. Unlike aggressive signals, which are always hostile, and affiliative signals, which are always approach/contact related, appeasement signals may serve an escape/avoidance function or an affiliative function. Dogs sometimes, but not always, use appeasement signals in order to encourage affiliative encounters (other times they use them when flight is impossible, in order to pacify a hostile encounter). The only common denominator in the use of appeasement signaling is that the individual seeks to escape or avoid some component of the encounter. This is a distance increasing function. If there is absolutely no reason to believe that the other individual may attack, there is no need for appeasement signals (O'Heare, 2007).

The Spaniel/Border Collie mix, offers an appeasing tongue flick, while the brown dog does a head turn, perhaps as a signal of disdain. There is no aggression apparent in this interaction, and yet neither dog appears to be clearly seeking an affiliative encounter. The Spaniel/Border Collie mix may be offering a ritualized greeting equivalent to "kneeling before the queen out of respect" (Sophia Yin, letter to author, December 31, 2007).

Lynn Crook

Appetitive Behavior:

(Also see *Aversion*)

"Activity that increases the likelihood of satisfying a specific need, as restless searching for food by a hungry predator" (Random House, Inc. on-line 2006).

> An *appetite* (italics theirs), so far as externally observable, is a state of agitation which continues so long as a certain stimulus, the appeted stimulus, is absent. When the appeted stimulus is at length received, it releases a consummator reaction, after which the appetitive behavior ceases and is succeeded by a state of relative rest, a state of satisfaction (Craig, 1917, page 685).

Arousal:

(Also see *Limbic System, Flared Whiskers, Penis Crowning*)

The state of being that occurs when strong emotions are evoked by *fear*, anger, stress, excitement, or joy. Arousal can be both pleasurable and distressing. Blink rate, *tongue flick* rate, and respiration rate increase during all states of arousal, but most acutely when arousal is uncomfortable. Indicators of stressful arousal take many forms: *piloerection, flared whiskers*, anal display, *penis crowning*, barking, whining, and other *vocalizations*. During heightened arousal, animals are predominantly reactive, the limbic system in the brain manages their fight or flight reactivity. During peek arousal, the animal may be unresponsive to attempts to elicit trained behaviors.

"Arousal is the general state of readiness to respond to the environment. Some degree of arousal is necessary for selective attention and purposeful responses" (Dee Ganley, letter to author, July 26, 2007).

> Arousal, like many other aspects of physiology in mammals, is regulated by mechanisms, much like the thermostat on the furnace in your home. It's the thermostat that keeps your furnace from staying on all the time: once the temperature rises to a certain level, a feedback system kicks in, and the heat is turned off. As the air in the house cools, then becomes too cold, the furnace kicks in again. In a healthy dog, emotional arousal is regulated in a similar way, with what are called the sympathetic and parasympathetic systems acting like thermostats to keep the body and brain functioning at optimal levels. But the body and brain can spiral out of control, if the circuits that control this kind of feedback don't have a chance to develop normally (McConnell, 2005, p. 81).

Monty Sloan

Note the many behaviors that convey arousal: piloerector reflex in both wolves, agonistic pucker – both wolves; paw over back – wolf on the left; paw-lift – wolf on the right.

Barbara Handelman

Two aroused dogs, tails raised high over their backs exposing their anuses. They are both standing tall, almost on tip toes; their bodies angled away from each other while they are nose-to-nose and making direct eye contact. The Lab has mild piloerection. Both have their ears high and alert.

Attack:

(Also see *Bite Inhibition, Predation*)

An actual attack might occur after numerous threats and other warning displays have been exhausted. Most attacks are ritualized aggression – they rarely escalate to the point of injury. When neither animal submits, or escape is impossible, an all-out attack may occur. All canids have the innate capacity to inflict severe injury on one another in a matter of seconds. The most severe injuries often occur in the area of the throat and over the spine. Wolves kill by crushing the trachea and causing suffocation, and inflict crippling wounds to the spinal cord of prey. Domestic dogs also go for the throat, legs, and abdomen, when they are intent on subduing or disabling an opponent. If dogs emerge from a fight uninjured, it is because one or both combatants have employed exquisite bite inhibition.

www.atourhands.com/fight.html#dog

This photo was taken during an organized "blood sport" event in Afghanistan. The dog on the right has intent to continue, probably until the death of the other dog who clearly has had enough. Note: Dog on left, whale eye caused by effort to watch his opponent while turning his head and body away, His ears are back and lips longer than his opponent's; mouth open wide as a defensive threat. The dog on right has short lips – commissure is forward indicative of continuing serious intent; ears forward and his jaws are aimed directly at the throat of his opponent.

Attend:

(See *Reproductive Behavior*)

Avoidance Behavior:

The canid uses positions or postures in order to avoid activity or environmental factors that cause him to feel stressed or fearful. While engaged in avoidance behaviors, the dog may be in "reactive" mode, not utilizing the thinking portion of his brain. Avoidance behaviors can also be a experientially learned or trained behavior. In which case, the dog's responses are cognitive rather than determined by "limbic" reactivity. For example, a dog may be taught to avoid engaging with other dogs by turning his attention to and making eye contact with his handler. Other avoidance behaviors: eyes averted, hiding, pressing into or against the human's body, turning away, leaving the situation.

Barbara Handelman

Louie presses against his person to relieve stress and avoid interacting.

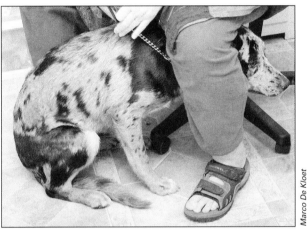

Jennifer Parizo

Dog experiencing extreme stress, avoiding interaction by pressing his body against the human. Note tail tuck and rounded back..

Marco De Kloet

Wicked is enthusiastically approaching a hound who changes directly so abruptly he nearly topples over in his effort to avoid Wicked's leap forward. There is no agonistic intent apparent in Wicked, his lips are long with his mouth partially open, his ears are relaxed. The whites of the hound's eyes are visible (this is not whale eye) as he keeps Wicked in his peripheral vision while abruptly changing direction to avoid Wicked. Both dogs are playing.

Marco De Kloet

Wicked, the Lurcher, usually up for any sort of rough play, appears intent on avoiding the exuberant spaniel. Wicked is doing a head turn, his ears are back and his body is angled away from the other dog to such a degree that he has crossed his front legs in order to maintain his balance.

Monty Sloan

Wolf on the left leaning away to avoid approaching wolf who is threatening with agonistic pucker, piloerection, hard stare and forward posture with weight directed toward the other wolf.

Bark Lunge:

(Also see *Barrier Aggression/Frustration, Distance Increasing Behaviors*)

Bark lunge behavior may begin as frustration from out-of-control exuberantly social behavior, and then build into *barrier aggression/frustration* when the animal's desire to interact is thwarted by restraint.

Aggressive dog does bark lunge towards another dog. Note tight lead intensifies his frustration. This is also a distance increasing behavior.

Dog on the left barks and lunges toward another dog at a dog park. She appears to have serious intent, her tail is held straight up, her ears are back, commisure is forward, and her hackles raised. The dogs she's approaching is attempting to diffuse the aggression by doing a slight head turn, and a paw-lift, her lips are longer with commisure farther back.

Bitch War:

(Also see *Intra-sex Aggressive Behavior*)

A commonly used slang term for the particularly fierce fights that occur between female dogs living in the same household.

Bite Inhibition:

(Also see *Acquired Bite Inhibition, Metasignals, Ritualized Aggression*)

Dogs may choose to employ exquisite control over the force they employ when using their mouths. During *Ritualized aggressive* interactions, dogs go through the same posturing, *jaw sparring*, and biting actions that they use during potentially lethal fights. Yet, they emerge from the *ritualized aggress*ive interactions having neither caused nor received so much as a scratch.

Bite inhibition may be employed in canid-to-canid interactions or in canid-to-human interactions. Ian Dunbar (2007) developed a scale for rating the seriousness of dog bites based on an assessment of the damage inflicted.

- **Level One:** Bark, lunge, and no teeth on skin.

- **Level Two:** Teeth touched, no puncture.

- **Level Three:** 1-4 holes from a single bite. All holes less than half the length of a single canine tooth.

- **Level Four:** Single bite, deep puncture (up to one and a half times the depth of a single canine tooth), black bruising, tears and/or slashing wounds. Dog clamped down and shook or slashed victim.

- **Level Five:** Multiple bite attack or multiple attack incidents.

- **Level Six:** Missing large portions of flesh, resulting in maiming or death of a canid or human.

In multiple dog attacks, different animals involved in the same attack may inflict differing levels of damage. Bite measurements and geometry must be compared to the wounds to properly assess the extent of each dog's involvement. In fatal attacks, it must be established exactly which dog/wound was the ultimate cause of death. DNA samples taken from the dogs' jaws and from the bite sites, before medical cleanup treatment, coupled with measurements and dental comparison, can establish this (Crosby, 2004, p. 2).

Barbara Handelman

Here are three examples of dogs and wolves using inhibited bites during ritualized aggression and social play.

Barbara Handelman

Monty Sloan

Body-Slam:

Body slams happen in the course of fairly rough play sessions. Some dogs enjoy this rough form of play, while others may simply tolerate it. Body-slams may cause *play* or *ritualized aggression* to evolve into *agonistic aggressive* reactivity, resulting in a fight. Body slams also occur as *agonistic behaviors* during real fights.

All photos this page by Marco De Kloet

Wicked, the Lurcher, body slams a much bigger dog with enough force to knock him off balance. Wicked then rolls the behemoth onto his back using his head.

Another body slam by Wicked, the Lurcher. He likes to play roughly with the big boys!

Bow:

(Also see *Play, Metasignals*)

> The bow is a stable posture from which the animal can move easily in many directions, allows the individual to stretch its muscles before and while engaging in play, and places the head of the bower below another animal in a non-threatening position (Bekoff, 1995, p. 5).

> Often referred to as a "play bow". It is a "transitional behavior" used for "punctuation" in the context of other behaviors – sometimes used in courtship, sometimes used in hunting, and sometimes used to initiate a "solicited bout" of play (Bekoff, 1995, p. 7).

While hunting wolves will "test" a prey animal by bowing in front of it, moving in and moving away, trying to assess the animal's vulnerability and cause the animal to turn and flee thus leaving its hind end vulnerable to attack. Such predatory behaviors are a common feature of canid play.

The bow position allows a canid with any degree of uncertainty to keep all his options open. From the bow posture, the canid can easily move in any direction.

Barbara Handelman

Bow as play interruption, metasignal .

Monty Sloan

Bow during hunt.

*Bow*s are *Metasignals*:

> ... Bows are used to maintain social play... when actions borrowed from other contexts, especially bites accompanied by rapid side to side shaking of the head, are likely to be misinterpreted.

> ... Bows might serve as a form of punctuation that clarifies the meaning of other actions that follow or precede them. In addition to sending the message "I want to play" when they are performed at the beginning of play, bows performed in a different context, namely during social play, might also carry the message "I want to play despite what I am going to do or just did – I still want to play" when there might be a problem in sharing this information between the interacting animals (Bekoff, 1995, p. 3).

Bow as play-soliciting metasignal.

Canids engaged in *predatory play*, *bow* to initiate a play session and to signal the moment when the roles of predator and prey switch from one dog (or group of dogs) to another.

Bowing may also be used to interrupt or "slowdown" escalating arousal levels.

Bow as metasignal that defuses rising tension and arousal.

Shoulder bow by very large dog helps puppy understand "this interaction is all play".

In the context of *courtship*, *bowing* is a display of interest and an invitation to interact.

Monty Sloan

Wolf on the left is bowing as part of a courtship display.

Barbara Handelman

Lear, the white dog, is bowing as a play interaction invitation along with direct eye contact. Pan, the Collie, appears slightly wary. He has dropped the ball he was carrying, offers a paw-lift, neutral ears, perhaps as distancing signals to tone down the intensity of the interaction a bit.

Boxing:

(Also see *Height Seeking*, *Sparring*, and *Foreleg Stab*)

Standing on hind legs, or rearing, is a common behavior during *ritualized aggression* – more so than during serious combat between canids. Some animals will use their front legs much as humans use their arms and hands to "punch" an opponent, and to block or avoid a bite or kick from their adversary.

Photos by Sabarika

Both dogs rear up and use their feet to block each other's blows.

Butt Sniff (slang term, properly called Perianal Investigation):

(Also see *Greeting Behaviors*)

Butt Sniffs during which dogs sniff the anus of another dog, are perhaps the most common form of dog-to-dog *greeting behavior*. Some dogs do a polite butt sniff, only taking a quick sniff in passing. Other dogs are rude – pressing their noses under the other dog's tail and doing more of an anal examination than a quick sniff.

A butt sniff train, with two dogs doing butt sniffs simultaneously to the dogs in front of them.

This is an investigatory greeting between two dogs who have played together before.

Black dog does butt sniff "on the fly"

Rude butt sniff by blue merle Aussie; red merle Aussie isn't pleased. He offers displacement behaviors – paw-lift and head turn – in response.

A Friendly Welcome

'Tis sweet to hear the watch-dog's honest bark
Bay deep-mouthed welcome as we draw near home;
'Tis sweet to know there is an eye will mark
Our coming, and look brighter when we come.

— George Gordon, Lord Byron

Section 4:
Cache – Displacement Behavior

Cache:

(Also see *Digging*)

Some dogs will cache, i.e. bury and hide food, bones, or prized toys. They retrieve the cached items later.

Among wolves and other predators, caching serves to protect food for later consumption by the procurer of the kill or his pack members. Burying food protects it from opportunistic scavengers, such as birds that quickly consume huge quantities of exposed food, but could not unearth a cached carcass.

During exceptionally cold weather, birds will consume large quantities of meat from a carcass wolves have temporarily abandoned. Scavenging by birds and other animals is one reason canids cache food.

Barbara Handelman

Calming Signals:

(Also see Displacement Behaviors, Distance Increasing Behaviors, Stress-Related Behaviors)

"Calming signals" is an umbrella term that came into popular usage among pet dog trainers after the publication of Turid Rugaas' book "On Talking Terms with Dogs: Calming Signals" (1997).

Ethologists have long recognized and categorized the same behaviors – using the terms *displacement behavior*, and *distance increasing behavior*, as well as identifying the many stress reactions that dogs portray using facial expressions and body posturing.

According to Rugaas: canids use specific signals to announce their own peaceful intentions to other canids and to people. Canids may use calming signals when they feel stressed, and when they perceive stress or threats in environment.

The signals may serve to calm the animal who is signaling, and calm others around him. Calming signals are used to avert potential threats. They are meant to convey goodwill, and the absence of threatening intentions. Rugaas explained that canids broadcast calming signals deliberately, to a non-specific audience, rather than to an individual recipient.

Previous page:
The coyote on the right is doing paw-over-back, and chin rest behaviors. These behaviors look affectionate, but the other coyote is doing a tongue flick and has airplane ears, suggesting she is experiencing emotional conflict about her companion's behavior.
Photo by Monty Sloan

Caution:

Canids display signs of caution when encountering new objects, or situations with which they are unfamiliar. Cautious displays include: braced front legs, ears forward, or angled backwards, intent visual focus, hesitance, and frozen animation. Weight is centered backwards away from the object that concerns the animal. Weight centered backwards generally belies lack of confidence and some degree of *fear*.

Coyote pups above display caution when approaching their first watermelon.

Puppy cautiously approaches a storm drain.

Chin-over:

A canid might place his head over the shoulders of another canid. The chin-over behavior appears during sexualized play, sexual approaches preceding mating, and during greetings. It is also seen as a means to assert control (*dominance*) over another dog.

Unneutered male Collie was determined to mount the neutered male border Collie. The chin-over back preceded riding up and mounting.

Chin-over dominance display after ritualized aggressive interaction.

Circle Investigation:

(Also see *Butt Sniff, Greeting Behaviors, Inguinal Sniff, Investigatory Behavior*)

"Simultaneous mutual rear investigation – Circle Investigation" (Donaldson, 2004, p. 77).

This is an example of an affiliative greeting called a "circle investigation" even though Pan, the Collie pup, is doing an inguinal sniff while Louie, the Gentle Giant, goes in for a butt sniff. In this configuration of body positions, Pan couldn't reach Louie's butt without a step ladder!

Clasp (Also Called a Hug):

(Also see *Sparring*, *Reproductive Behavior*)

Pat Goodman, wolf behaviorist at Wolf Park, calls this behavior a "hug." Defining it in the *Ethogram*, she writes:

> To clasp around the neck or shoulders using one or both front legs. It is accompanied by greeting behavior or submissive expressive behavior and there is no pelvic thrusting. Once in a while a hug will be used to hold the head or neck of an opponent still (Goodman, et al. 2002, p. 15).

Dogs engaged in ritualized aggression. The Great Dane is clasping the other dog during ritualized aggression.

Clasp during jaw sparring.

Two dogs do one-legged clasps around the shoulders of their sparring partner.

Clasp preparatory to mating.

63

Commissure of the Lips:

Anatomy – There are many points in the body where two surfaces meet and form commissures. These include anywhere eyelids, lips, or cardiac valves join or form a connection. Throughout this book, "commissure" refers to the commissure of the lips.

Observing the commissure of a dog's lips reveals essential information about *aggression* and other emotional states. In a dog with serious aggressive intent, the oral commissure is drawn forward. In dogs at play, or engaged in *ritualized aggressive behavior,* the mouth will be more widely open and the commissure is drawn back farther.

Agonistic puckers occur both during *ritualized aggression* and *aggression* with intent to threaten harm. The length of the commissure of the lips should not be relied upon to determine the seriousness of a dog's intention to bite. Like most signals, the length of the commissure of the lips must be observed in the context of all the concurrent signals a dog is offering in any given moment.

Monty Sloan

Lips are short, and commissure is forward in this agonistic pucker. This is a serious warning, threat.

Sabarika

The Lab's lips are long and the commissure is widened into a c-shape. This is a less serious warning than the one issued by the wolf.

Jennifer Parizo

This dog's lips are short, commissure is forward. The agonistic pucker is just beginning. This was a serious threat that was followed by a snap.

Communication:

Dogs use their bodies to communicate, purposefully. If a person watches dogs long enough, she learns that almost nothing a dog does is either incidental or accidental. When a dog's actions or postures cause another dog to change its behavior, the dogs are communicating.

> Communication presupposes at least three factors: a sender, a receiver and a signal. Signals are received through the senses of sight, hearing, touch, taste and smell. Signals may be facial expressions, barking, licking, or chemical substances, such as the urine of a female in heat (Abrantes, 1997, p. 75).

Effective canine communication depends on the receiver understanding the messages sent by the canid.

Canids communicate deliberately in order to convey information about themselves or the environment, and to alter behavior in another dog or human. Not all communication emanates from deliberate behavior. When canids show signs of fear, those signs are not deliberate. They are received as communication from the other canids and humans around them. Autonomic responses are physical responses that convey information. And while autonomic responses are not deliberate or under voluntary control they do convey information to others in the environment. Examples: respiration or heart rates increase or decrease in relation to stress; panting, eyes dilating or contracting, *piloerector reflex* (*raised hackles*), drooling, trembling, etc. Canids are limited to modes of communication by their anatomy. Through voluntary muscle control, they create a wide range of expressions, using postures and movement of specific body parts to express a full range of emotions. They also express vocal sounds, but do not have structures of oral language.

There are different types of information that can influence dogs' communication behaviors:

Contextual cues: Contextual cues are any stimuli in the local environment. For example: the sound of food bowls clanking, or a can opener touching a can, would signal dinner preparation. Dogs might come from afar and begin jockeying for position to be fed first.

Signals: Specific acts performed by one animal (canid or human) that convey information to another.

Displays: are signals that have evolved by natural selection to enhance the transfer of information. Displays are distinct communicative behaviors on the part of the sender. See *ritualization* below.

Compulsive Disorders:

Compulsive Disorders in canids are similar to "obsessive compulsive disorder" in humans. Dogs respond to some of the same behavior modification and drug therapies as humans.

The current theory is that altered metabolism of the neurotransmitter serotonin is responsible for the development and maintenance of compulsive disorders in dogs. So, it is truly a brain disorder and not just a behavior problem.

Diagnostic Characteristics of canine Compulsive Disorders

- The behavior is an out-of-context repetition of normal behaviors.

- The behavior may be associated with a specific triggering event.

- The behavior has no obvious purpose.

- The behavior may harm the dog's health.

- The behavior is shown, even though the original conflict or frustration has been eliminated.

- The dog seems unable to control the behavior.

- The dog may seem anxious or frustrated.

- The behavior occurs often enough to interfere with the pet's ability to function normally.

- The behavior prevents normal interaction between the dog and its family (Muns, 2004, p. 1, 6).

Conspecific:

A member of the same species.

Consummatory Behavior:

(Also see *Consummatory Face* and *Instinct*)

"A behavior pattern that occurs in response to a stimulus and that achieves the satisfaction of a specific drive, as the eating of captured prey by a hungry predator (distinguished from *appetitive behavior*)". Dictionary.com Unabridged (v 1.1) Based on the Random House Unabridged Dictionary, Random House, Inc. 2006.

Consummatory Face:

Consummate means complete or perfect in every respect: as in consummate happiness. The consummatory face can be seen when a dog satisfyingly scratches a particularly itchy itch. The dog's face is characteristically tilted upward, lips drawn straight back and closed; the mouth may fall open but no teeth are deliberately exposed.

Both dogs display consummatory faces – eyes are squinty, faces tilted upwards, long loose lips pulled straight back, ears relaxed.

Coprophagia:

(Also see *Pica*)

Eating feces of the animal's own species or the feces of other species. It may even include a canid eating his own feces. Coprophagia is a normal feature of maternal care of infant canids. Initially, the pups cannot defecate or urinate on their own. The mother must lick the anus to stimulate defecation. She then eats the feces to keep the nest or bedding clean.

Bianca and Lear begin eating the feces of other dogs before it can hit the ground. Such determination makes management of the problem nearly impossible, unless the dogs are kept in separate pens, which is impractical.

Cruising Behavior:

(Also see *Temperament*)

Cruising behavior is a popular, descriptive term, not one supported by scientific investigation. Livestock guardian dogs will typically cruise any new environment to acquaint themselves with the territory, its boundaries, and potential threats to the animals in their care. This behavior can be seen even in young puppies. Cruising is a *characteristic behavior* for livestock guardian dogs. It is important to note that there are behaviors specific to certain breeds or classes of dogs. People who evaluate the *temperament* of puppies or adult dogs need to be aware of breed specific behaviors. Otherwise, they risk interpreting a behavior such as cruising, as aloofness, or lack of *affiliative* interest.

These two eight-week-old Great Pyrenees puppies are cruising an unfamiliar room during the start of their temperament evaluations. Only after they had investigated the perimeter, did they cheerfully respond to the evaluator's invitations to cuddle and play.

Crouch:

When crouching, the canid's legs are bent and his body is lowered. A crouch can be differentiated from a *stalk* by the fact that while crouching, the canids back is arched or rounded and his head is usually lower than the topline of his body, ears are back and tail lowered or tucked between his legs.

The wolf on the right assumes a crouching posture as he moves away from the dominant wolf on the left. Note: drooping tail, rounded back, and lowered head.

Curving Body Lines:

(Also see *Displacement Signals*)

When dogs approach others indirectly with distinct curving lines to their bodies, the curves convey the absence of intent to threaten or harm and thus serve as *displacement signals*.

Cursorial:

(Also see *Predation* and *Rolling*)

Definition: *Cursorial*: "adapted for running" (Hildebrande, 1988)

Canids are cursorial hunters. Their bodies are built for running. When hunting prey larger than themselves, "they run their prey down" which means to run them to the point of exhaustion. Once the prey is exhausted, the canid will attack and bring the animal down. Canids do not "hamstring" their prey because to do so would leave them vulnerable to crippling kicks from the powerful prey animals. Canids are not stealth hunters. They stalk and test the herd in order to pick out the weakest, most vulnerable member as their prey. According to Pat Goodman (2007, Wolf Park Behavior Seminar), "it is a myth that canids roll in the scent of carrion or feces to mask their own scent in order not to be detected by their prey. They don't need to mask their own odor, because they do not sneak up on prey."

According to Mech (1979) wolves do try to get close enough to be able to keep pace with and potentially exhaust their prey. Moose are the largest mammals wolves hunt. Wolves and moose both attain a maximum running speed of 35 mph. They are well matched in that respect, which is why wolves are most successful in catching and killing young, elderly, or injured animals.

Even a kick from a bison calf can be dangerous, a good reason not to try to hamstring prey.

Lure coursing greyhounds about to chase down a rabbit.

Cut-Off Signals:

(Also see *Calming Signals, Distance Increasing Signals,* and *Freezes*)

Cut-offs are behaviors similar to *displacement* and *distance increasing behaviors,* but are usually seen in combinations of multiple simultaneous signals. Canids use cut-offs to interrupt behavior coming at them from another animal. Cut-off displays unequivocally signal that further interaction is not desired. Cut-off signals are triggered by conflict. If cut-off signals are not respected, conflict will escalate.

Cut-off signals generally include two or more of the following behaviors: dramatic *head turn*s; turning the body away; *turning the back* to other animals, moving away, *freezes, agonistic pucker,* growling, *hackles raised,* averting eyes, lowered head, C-Curves, *pinning* after conflict.

Moments earlier these three dogs were playing raucously. When the play became too intense, they stopped and moved off separately with their backs to each other.

Both the Great Dane and the Pit Bull are signaling their desire to interrupt the interaction between them. The Dane's body is curving away from the Pit Bull, while the Pit Bull does a tongue flick.

Two dogs freeze for an instant before resuming play.

Wolf pup on the left responds to his littermate's threatening agonistic pucker by dramatically turning his body away, to signal his desire to end the interaction.

Demeanor Shifting:

(Also see *Play Skill Deficits, Ritualized Aggression* and *Play*)

During play, demeanor shifting occurs when dogs change roles. The dominant dog becomes submissive; the chaser becomes the one who is chased; the predator becomes the prey, etc. Failure to signal a change of roles, or to actually change roles after a playmate has signaled the desire to do so, may result in the interaction escalating and tipping over into a real fight (Donaldson, 2004, p. 77).

Digging:

(Also see *Cache*)

Digging is behavior with many different motivations. First and foremost, digging is natural behavior for dogs. It may, however, be perceived as a problem severe enough in the eyes of the human caretakers that they consider re-homing or euthanasia.

Barbara Handelman

Puppy digging recreationally.

Some breeds dig to hunt for food. Dachshunds and many terriers, in particular, have been bred to "go to ground" after prey (*ingestion behavior*).

Often, animals will dig to create a cool place for sleeping and shelter (et-epimeletic – comfort seeking). Digging may serve as a recreational relaxation behavior that relieves the stress of boredom. It may be an *allelomimetic behavior,* i.e. they do it because other dogs around them are digging too. Some dogs dig as an *investigatory behavior* – there might be an interesting smell in the location, or the ground has already been disturbed by a gardener, making it especially interesting.

Digging might also be a *reproductive behavior,* as when a bitch prepares a nest for her pups. Digging may occur during *barrier frustration* when the dog is trying to get at an intruder on the other side of a fence or gate.

Some dogs might dig to hide (*cache*) a bone, a prized toy or food (self care).

Sabarika

This dog is investigating a scent or unearthing something she or another canid cached in the past. In either case, she appears to have "lost her head" with enthusiasm for the project.

Marco De Kloet

These two dogs are digging in unison. It is not clear what inspired the dogs to start digging. It is likely that this is allelomemetic behavior, in which the second dog is digging because the other one started.

Dimorphism:

Physical and behavioral characteristics, other than sexual organs, that differentiate the male and female members of a species, such as: bone mass, breadth of the head, overall body size; coat color or plumage and vocalizations, especially of birds and moose, Dogs are not very dimorphic (Sophia Yin, letter to author, December 31, 2007).

Displacement Behavior:

(Also see *Calming Signals, Cut-Off Signals, Distance Increasing Behaviors, Displacement Disorders, Indicators of Stress*)

Displacement behaviors get their name from the fact that they appear displaced, or out of context when they occur. Displacement behaviors occur because of conflicting or frustrated impulses to perform behaviors that are impeded. Displacement behaviors also occur when the animal experiences simultaneous conflicting emotional states and cannot figure out what else to do.

Displacement behaviors arise from situations of either conflict or frustration. When an animal may be motivated to perform two or more behaviors that are in conflict with each other (e.g. approach-withdrawal, greeting but fear of being punished). The inability to perform both of the strongly motivated behaviors can lead to conflict resulting in the performance of a displacement behavior. Similarly, when an animal is prevented or frustrated from performing a highly motivated behavior (e.g. territorial aggression but dog is behind a barricade), a displacement behavior can also be observed. Displacement behaviors are usually normal behaviors that are shown at an inappropriate time, appearing out of context for the occasion (Overall & Landsberg, 2002).

Dogs use displacement behaviors when they are feeling stressed or uncertain. By engaging in a familiar behavior (usually one not stimulated by or relevant to the immediate environmental context), the dog can distract himself from and avoid responding to whatever caused his stress.

Displacement behaviors are a reflection of the dog's internal emotional state, rather than a deliberate attempt to signal information to others.

"Most, if not all, displacement behaviors are 'voluntary' behaviors, e.g. sniffing or scratching" (Lore I. Haug, letter to author, August 2007).

Some dogs will interrupt play, or other types of interactions with humans or other dogs, to take a quick "inventory" of their own uro-genital body parts. This is a form of displacement behavior that appears most in stressful situations.

Barbara Handelman

Dog on the left doing an uro-genitial body check as a displacement behavior.

Barbara Handelman

Louie is doing a bow, which serves as displacement behavior.

Elizabeth Way

Two eight-month-old littermates are playing roughly, while Lear, also a littermate, scratches. Lear's scratching is a displacement behavior that expresses Lear's indecision or conflict. He may be trying to decide whether or not to join his siblings in their rough play.

Barbara Handelman

Two adolescent dogs have just been playing together; their play behaviors included signs of mounting tension between them. They stopped to rest in very close proximity to each other and their people. They are both performing displacement behaviors – Louie is sniffing the ground, Cary has turned his head away. Cary's dramatic yawn is an indicator of stress. Displacement behaviors in this context suggest that neither dog is comfortable, but does not know what to do next.

Barbara Handelman

Sniffing

Monty Sloan

Wolf on left sniffing. Wolf on right stretching, and blinking.

The one absolutely unselfish friend that man can have in this selfish world, the one that never deserts him, the one that never proves ungrateful or treacherous, is his dog.

– Samuel Coleridge

I think we are drawn to dogs because they are the uninhibited creatures we might be if we weren't certain we knew better.

– George Bird Evans

Section 5:
Distance – Distress

Critical Distance:

"When flight distance is overstepped, as occurs when an animal is cornered, we speak of the critical distance. The critical reaction may be triggered, which is usually an explosive attack." (Klinghammer, 1992, p. 6)

Flight Distance:

"The distance you can get to an animal before it flees. Zero flight distance = you can touch the animal" (Sophia Yin, letter to author, December 31, 2007)

"Flight is hazard avoidance behavior, an essential component of a wild animal's survival. There are two measurable components to flight distance: 1) how close you can get to the animal before it attempts to flee, and 2) how far away it runs" (Coppinger, 2001, p. 64).

Flight distance is significant when frightened canids are approached either by another animal or a person. The canid who cannot flee is likely to feel trapped. If the canid's ability to flee is blocked or even inhibited, he may respond with *aggressive behavior*.

Being on leash, in a crate, or within a fenced area, can prevent a dog from fleeing. Encounters with strange dogs or unusual objects (e.g. flapping laundry on a line, or a big, overturned trash can in its path) can also trigger a dog's impulse to flee, and evoke an aggressive response if the dog cannot flee because it is on leash.

Social Distance:

Social distance refers to the physical distance individuals require to feel comfortable within a group or pack. People also have a social distance comfort zone, usually referred to as "personal space". Although a person might not be able to define "personal space" in terms of inches or feet, he or she can readily identify the moment when another person crosses the boundary.

People and canids alike will move away from the individual who violates the social distance comfort zone.

Opposite Page:
Fox is doing a paw-lift with intense stare.
This combination of behaviors suggests that
these are distance increasing behaviors.
Photo by Barbara Handelman

Distance Decreasing Behaviors:

Distance decreasing behaviors convey deference and peaceful intentions that invite other canids, humans, or animals of other species to come closer, without fearing attack. Such behaviors include:

Ears Forward
Open Mouth with Long Lips

Hip Nudge

Muzzle Nudge

Paw-lift
Paw-lift in this instance is part of an affiliative approach.

Play Bow
Play Face

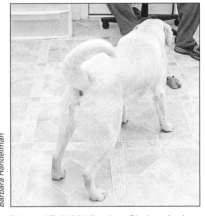

Relaxed Tail Whirling in a Circle – dog's butt might also be wagging

Submissive Grin

Distance Increasing Behaviors:

(Also see *Cut-Offs*)

Distance increasing behaviors signal that an interaction may be too intense or prolonged for one canid's comfort. He uses a variety of signals to let other canids, humans and animals of other species know that they should back off, or end the interaction.

Agonistic Pucker

Ears Flattened or Pressed Back

Intent stare. A bark and lunge followed.

Crouch Head Lower Than Body, Tail Down, Legs Bent

Head Turn/Turn Away
Tail lowered

Height Seeking Posture
Louie: height seeking posture, mouth closed, tail raised
Cary: doing a muzzle punch

Low Tone Vocalization (low growl). Punctuated Barking (repeating same sound, barking intended to give the message "go away, go away". Carlos the Cocker barks repeatedly as he runs.

Splitting
Pan does a split to increase the distance between two other dogs.

79

Marco De Kloet

Wicked, the Lurcher, is offering several simultaneous distance increasing signals. He does a bark lunge, hard stare, and agonistic pucker with ears back. The target of these behaviors seems relatively unconcerned. Note his forward ears, and stillness. Perhaps he is reading the fact that Wicked has a slight curve to his body and long lips with the commissure quite far back. These metasignals suggest that his threats will not be followed by an immediate attack. Backing off or ending the encounter would still be wise.

Marco De Kloet

This dramatic paw-lift is a distance increasing behavior; the dog also has alert, forward ears, and an intent stare. The paw-lift in this instance warns dogs in the distance to stay away.

Distress:

(Also see *Eustress* and *Stress*)

Distress... means a damaging excess burden on the organism. During the past few decades, stress has been predominantly connected with a reduction in well-being, efficiency and health. In other words: references to stress practically always mean distress (Scholz and Reinhardt, 2007, p. 9).

My little dog – a heartbeat at my feet.

– Edith Wharton

A dog has the soul of a philosopher.   – Plato

Until he extends the circle of his compassion to all living things, man will not himself find peace.

– Dr. Albert Schweitzer

Section 6: Domestication – External Stimuli

Domestication:

(Also see *Neoteny, Heterochrony, Paedomorphosis*)

Price (1984) defined domestication as "a process by which a population of animals becomes adapted to man and the captive environment by some combination of genetic changes occurring over generations and environmentally induced developmental events recurring during each generation."

Archeological evidence proves that thousands of years ago Stone Age humans and wolves began to live in close association. It is unclear whether humans chose wolves as hunting companions, or whether wolves chose humans because proximity to their villages meant easier access to food. The truth probably lies in a combination of the two, because both humans and wolves profited from the association. Many scientists believe that domestication of wolves (*Canis lupus*) resulted in the emergence of *Canis familiaris*, the domesticated dog. The domesticated dog is an extremely close relative of the gray wolf, differing from it by at most 0.2% of mtDNA (mitochondrial DNA) sequence (Wayne, www.idir. net/~wolf2dog/wayne2.htm).

Domestication has brought with it many obviously visible changes to size, shape, color, coat length and coat type within dog breeds. Other, not so easily identified changes, some positive, some detrimental, have occurred as well. Those changes include, but are not limited to:

1. *Paedomorphosis*: "the retention of juvenile morphology at maturity, is thought to be an important process in generating evolutionary novelties" (Goodwin, et al., 1997, p. 297).

2. Female wolves are monoestrus (fertile only once a year), while dogs are bi-estrus (fertile periods twice a year).

3. Male wolves are only fertile (only produce sperm) at the season when female wolves are fertile. Male dogs produce sperm all the time, unless neutered.

   Male and female wolves are not sexually mature until they are twenty-two months old; dogs are sexually mature by one year of age or younger.5. Behaviorally, dogs are less likely than wolves to inhibit aggression, or use ritualized aggressive behaviors to resolve conflicts, than are wolves. Dogs depend on human intervention before and after dog-to-dog conflicts to prevent or heal wounds. Wolves avoid injurious attacks by engaging in ritualized aggression (Goodwin, et al. 1996, p. 302).

The relative infrequency and intensity of injurious fights among wolves may also reflect their retention of sensitivity to signaling from other wolves.

Opposite Page: One wolf standing over another may be a display of dominance, as it is in this instance. The wolf beneath protests with a "push off" while at the same time displaying submission by rolling over. Note: the standing wolf's dominance displays a raised tail, forward ears, and piloerector reflex, while using no physical force.
Photo by Monty Sloan

"Wolves and wild animals do fight (and get kicked out of their social groups). They don't fight as much as they would if they were unable to leave their social group (the way dogs are)" (Sophia Yin, letter to author, December 31, 2007)

> Domestication has also led to social changes in dogs. For instance, although wolves live in tightly knit family units called packs, free-ranging dogs exhibit more variability in social behaviors, with many dogs living in small loosely structured groups that may be temporary rather than stable pack-like groups. Along with less rigid grouping, dogs have a tempered drive to attain high rank. (Yin, 2007, p. 416)

It is important to note that tameness (zero *flight distance*) occurs within a single animal's lifetime while domestication occurs over many generations.

Dominance:

(Also see *Piloerector Reflex, Ritualized Aggression, Submission, Social Hierarchies*)

Dominance is a description of status within a stable canine social hierarchy. A dominant canid controls priority access to a range of resources including food, choice sleeping spaces, and breeding rights. The dominant individual may – from time to time – chose to relinquish, or bestow on others, any of his specific privileges of rank without jeopardizing his status within the social group.

> Dominance is a quality of a relationship between individuals. Dominance cannot exist in isolation and you may be a dominant individual in one relationship but not in another (Horwitz, November 1, 2006 radio broadcast).

> A dominance – submission training model is irrelevant for most of the behaviors people want from their animals, such as coming when called, walking calmly on a leash, and generally calm behavior. Consequently, using aggression and the dominance theory to address most undesirable behaviors in dogs is inappropriate (Yin, 2007, p. 415).

When the term "dominance" refers to "status" it assumes a long-standing, consistent relationship between individuals – one of whom "wins" in *ritualized aggressive* displays, while the other regularly, and voluntarily submits.

Dominance displays or contests among dogs, or within wolf packs, may serve as tests of relative physical fitness and confidence.

Dangerous fights can erupt when one canid fails to heed the warnings issued by another; when either canid cannot escape from the ritualized altercation; or when humans interfere with normal social interactions. Alternatively, fights can erupt when owners fail to intervene when highly aroused or socially inappropriate dogs are escalating in arousal and confrontation.

Canids born and raised with their littermates identify with other canids during their earliest days of life. Puppies learn how other canids smell, look, feel and act. Humans do not smell, act or feel like canids. Humans lack the facial muscles required to curl their lips, or flatten their ears against their heads. Although humans do have *piloerector reflexes*, they lack the coat with which to create a display of *hackles*. Thus, humans cannot replicate the *ritualized aggressive* postures and expressions with which canids resolve most conflicts.

Benevolent leadership establishes a healthy relationship between canids and humans.

"Leadership is the ability to influence others to perform behaviors that they would not necessarily perform on their own" (Yin, 2007, p. 415).

A strong human leader shows the dog what behavior is desirable or undesirable by bestowing or withholding resources.

Leadership is established when the owner can set clear limits for the dog's behavior and can effectively communicate the rules by always rewarding correct behaviors as they occur while preventing or immediately removing the rewards for undesirable behaviors, before they are accidentally reinforced. The owners must reward the desired behaviors frequently enough that they become habits. When owners can meet these criteria, their dogs will consider them to be predictable, dependable, and trustworthy (Yin, 2007, p. 417).

Dominance is clearly portrayed in the upright, forward-moving posture of the wolf on the left. The wolf on the right shares responsibility for the outcome of the interaction by clearly displaying submission: back arched, tail tucked, front paw lifted. No physical contact or force transpired between the two wolves, because they have already worked out their relationship.

The wolf on the left displays dominance using tall posture, raised tail, neutral ears and no agonistic pucker. The wolf on the right is displaying submissive-aggression with a threatening agonistic pucker. The outcome of the interaction is determined through displays alone; no physical force is required to maintain the established pack order between the alpha wolf on the left and his subordinate on the right.

Monty Sloan

Ruedi, the Omega wolf, consistently at the bottom of the pack's social hierarchy, submits to Wotan, one of the Beta wolves in the pack. Notice Wotan's stiff upright posture, hackles raised and tail slightly higher than his top line. Both wolves are doing head turns. Reudi has assumed a submissive posture lying on his side, but he is also using his legs to brace against Wotan in a half-hearted effort to fend him off.

Monty Sloan

Wotan strikes a dominant posture over Renki who is lower in the pack's social hierarchy. Notice that Wotan is leaning forward towards Renki, with hackles raised. Renki's submissive posturing is dramatic – his tail is tucked totally under him as he crouches, rounds his back, turns his head, and lifts a front paw. Kailani watches in the background.

Epimeletic Behavior:

(Also see *Allogrooming, Nibble Groom, Maternal Behavior, Scoot*)

Epimeletic Behaviors include all acts of self-care and caring for others.

Examples:

- **Self-care:** grooming, *nibble grooming*, and licking genitals

- **Grooming:** companion

- *Maternal behaviors*: such as licking to elicit elimination, allowing puppies to nurse, carrying puppies, regurgitating food for puppies

- **Food caching**

- **Shelter building:** turning around before lying down, *digging* bed in dirt, *digging* to enlarge den.

Grooming companion – allelomimetic behavior

Licking puppy to stimulate elimination

Self-care licking genitals

Self-care: lick grooming.

Monty Sloan

Self-care: face washing while standing using paw dampened with snow and saliva.

Monty Sloan

Wicked is cleaning a cut on his foot. This is a form of epimeletic, self-care behavior. All dogs will clean their own wounds. Some will clean the wounds of their canine and human companions, if allowed to.

Monty Sloan

Self-care: face wipe in the snow.

Monty Sloan

Self-care: face washing using a paw dampened with saliva.

Shelter seeking is a form of comfort-seeking behavior

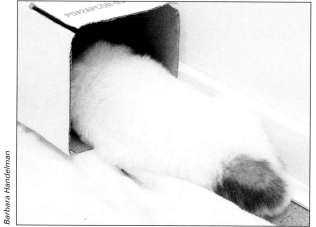

A puppy takes a nap inside a box he has chosen for shelter.

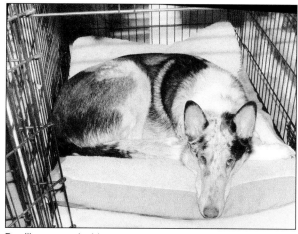

Pan likes to nap inside an open crate.

A wolf seeks the cool shelter of a hollow log, for relaxation on a hot summer day.

Epiphenomenon:

A secondary phenomenon that occurs alongside a primary phenomenon.

Examples: *hackles* raised (*piloerection*) that occurs along with other indicators of arousal or stress such as *stress panting, ears flattened, agonistic pucker, lip licking, paw-lift, head lowered*, etc.

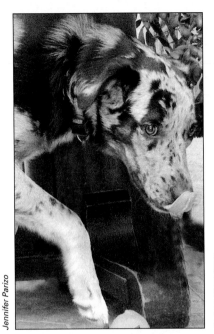

Jennifer Parizo

Barbara Handelman

Sabarinka

For this frightened dog the exaggerated paw-lift is the primary phenomenon while the accompanying signals – lowered head, lip licking, dilating eyes, tension ridges in his face, short tense lips – are the epiphenomena.

Dog expressing conflicting emotions of fear and aggression: the exaggerated open-mouthed agonistic pucker is the primary phenomenon while the accompanying paw-lift, raised tail, hard eyes (squinting with scowl lines between his eyes) one ear erect, the other lowered and back are the epiphenomena.

This dog is appears to be displaying mixed emotions. The agonistic pucker appears to be the primary phenomenon, since it is accompanied by a forward commissure, and hard eyes (furrows appear between the eyes). The shake off is the epiphenomenon, and may be a displacement behavior suggesting lack of confidence or conflict about the apparent intensity of his threat. Then again, he may be shaking off because he is wet.

Et-Epimeletic Behavior:

(Also see *Muzzle Nudge, Pawing, Redirected Behavior, Regurgitate*)

Et-epimeletic behaviors are all behaviors that solicit comfort, food, or affection, from *conspecifics* or humans.

Examples: Puppy licking to elicit regurgitation, whining, yelping, *tail wagging*, licking the face or hand of person, usually with *tail wagging*.

Puppy muzzle nudges, left and right, a normal puppy greeting behavior toward humans or conspecifics.

Wolf pups solicit regurgitated food from an uncle.

Ethogram:

A tool used by ethologists where all observed behaviours of a particular species are listed. Observations of particular individuals or groups of individuals can then be charted against a master list and graphed. Detailed analysis of Ethograms can yield valuable information such as energy budgets, amount of time spent on a given behaviour and sequencing of behaviors. (Sue Alexander, letter to author, August 14, 2007).

Ethology:

E.O. Wilson, Professor Emeritas at Harvard University, and the father of Sociobiology says: "Ethology is the systematic study of the behavior of animals under natural conditions" (2004).

Ethology is a branch of zoology.

Ethologists and behaviorists both study animal behavior. Behaviorists primarily confine their work to scientific studies in controlled laboratory environments. Ethologists study animals "in the field" or in environments more natural to the animal than a laboratory.

Eustress:

(Also see *Distress* and *Stress*)

Eustress is a necessary activation of the organism allowing the animal (or the human) to use its energies optimally and thus also enabling the development of capabilities (Scholz and Reinhardt, 2007, p. 9).

Evolutionary Continuity:

If we look hard enough, we can find the roots of our own intelligence and emotions in other animals. Again, this doesn't mean that humans and other animals are identical, but rather that they share enough common physical or functional traits that their capacities fall on a continuum. That's what "evolutionary continuity" refers to: the similarities and contrasts among species are nuances or shades of gray, not stark black-and-white differences (Bekoff, 2007, p. 33).

Evolutionary Roots of Behavior:

Animals are divided into groups by their external (appearance – *morphology*) and internal (physiologic) characteristics. According to Dr. Erich Klinghammer, Founder and Director of Wolf Park, species can also be identified and classified by behavioral patterns that are unique, such as:

...distinct vocalizations, types of food eaten, techniques for finding or hunting food, unique social organizations, defense against predators, and learning abilities limited to certain tasks.

These unique species, genus, or family characteristics are the building blocks for an animal's specific life style. These behavior patterns, as well as recognition of food, shelter, or fellow species members, is (sic) often inborn: i.e. does not have to be learned after birth by the individual. All the animal needs is to be in the appropriate situation in which specific signals or releasers are present, and the behavior is elicited. This means that much of the behavior we encounter is part of the animal's repertoire prior to any experiences since birth which may affect present behavior (Klinghammer, 1992, p. 1-2).

Excretory (Also Called Eliminative Behavior):

(Also see *Et-Epimeletic Behaviors*, *Investigatory Behavior*)

Excretory behaviors include all forms of bodily elimination, and defecation.

Males: urinate with all 4 legs extended; or while lifting one hind leg, to direct the urine stream to places where other animals have left their mark. (See *Over–marking.*)

Six-week-old male puppy urinating.

Ten-week-old male puppy urinating.

Adult male wolf urinating with hind leg raised slightly and stretched out behind him.

Male dog on left doing a very high leg lift to leave his scented "calling card" as high up on the bone statue as he can reach. He is over-marking.

Male wolf urinating with his hind leg tucked up as high as he can get it, directing his urine stream against the side of the water trough.

Females: commonly urinate in a squatting position; may lift one hind leg to over-mark where another animal has left scent before her; similarly, a female might back up against a post, tree or other object to direct her urine stream to leave her mark in a specific location.

Some other female urination postures include:

1. Squat-raise (squat with one hind leg lifted up)

2. Squat, no leg raised

3. Raise (standing with one hind leg raised)

4. Flex raise (the above but with the other back leg slightly flexed so the butt is squatted toward the ground just a little)

5. Elevated (resembles a typical male dog marking posture with leg raised above horizontal)

6. Handstand

The female wolf on top of the stump in female urination posture #5.

Female fox, squat urination position #2.

Kailani demonstrates handstand urination, position #6. This position tends to be preformed by high strung females who are easily aroused. The choice of this particular marking behavior is most likely not a conscious or premeditated act, rather it is a sign of arousal which might have various causes. In this instance, Kailani was in heat. Her arousal reflects her own hormonal state and the attention she was receiving from the males in her pack.

Defecating:

Puppy defecating.

Both genders: wander, nose the ground before defecation – scratching the ground with all four feet following defecation is most common in males but also seen in females.

External Stimuli:

A stimulus that is external to the animal. External stimuli can be divided into those that will trigger behaviours (release *fixed action patterns*); those that may elicit interest or curiosity or even exploration; and those that are not relevant to the animal (Sue Alexander, letter to author, August 14, 2007).

Key Stimuli:

Dr. Erich Klinghammer discusses specific types of external stimuli that release behaviors during canine development.

Some of these specific stimuli are called key stimuli, suggesting the precise fit of a key into a lock to unlock the appropriate behavior.

Social Releasers: Signals that come from a member of the animal's own species (*conspecific*) are called "social releasers".

Intra-specific Releasers: Some signals only effect *conspecifics* (members of the same species) and are thus called intra-specific releasers.

Inter-specific Releasers: Other signals like alarm calls, are inter-specific releasers. Thus the alarm call of one species might be understood by members of another species (Klinghammer, 1992, p. 2).

I have sometimes thought of the final cause of dogs having such short lives, and I am quite satisfied it is in compassion to the human race; for if we suffer so much in losing a dog after an acquaintance of ten or twelve years, what would it be if they were to live double that time.

– Sir Walter Scott

The two dogs in the foreground freeze during a face off. Note that both dogs display whale eye, and both have ears angled back. The black dog's whiskers are angled forward, indicating stress arousal. In contrast, notice the two dogs in the background. Both are doing head turns, as displacement signals, and Wicked, the Lurcher on the left, is doing a paw-lift. Compared to the two engaged in the face off, the two dogs in the background are quite relaxed.

Photo by Marco De Kloet

Section 7:
Face Off – Functional Systems

Face Off:

Canids use face to face, direct eye contact judiciously. Direct eye contact is usually perceived as a challenge by other canids, and can lead to an all out battle, if not accompanied by sufficient *metasignals* to inform the recipient that the direct eye contact is intended as play or *ritualized aggression.*

Barbara Handelman

Two relaxed and playful dogs face each other, making direct eye contact, watching to see which of them will make the next move to launch them into a ritualized (playful) sparring match. This is not a freeze – note that both dogs have long and relaxed lips, their mouths are open, and their ears are alert – neither pressed back nor forward in a manner that would suggest agonistic intent.

Two males face off over the back of a female in season.

Bison and stalking wolf – facing off.

Two wolves face off and challenge each other with direct eye contact. Notice the squinty eyes and furrows between the eyes of the wolf on the left. Neither has yet issued a threat, but either one might turn away or threaten in the seconds that follow.

Facial Markings:

(Also see *Agonistic Pucker, Paedomorphosis*)

Markings, especially those around the eyes, help canids interpret the information conveyed via facial expressions. Canids with solidly black faces tend to be much more difficult for humans and canids alike, to "read". Canids tend to be more reactive upon first meeting a black faced dog, than when first encountering an animal with markings that help the eyes stand out from the rest of the face. Humans also tend to have more fearful reactions to black faced dogs than to dogs with distinctive facial markings.

The small brown spots above the eyebrow ridge of Rottweillers helps to differentiate one facial expression from another.

These two Collies have distinctive facial markings, including large eyebrow patches that contrast with the colors surrounding the eyes, making their facial expressions very easy to read.

These wolf pups have distinctive circles around each eye as well as "eye-liner" markings at the corner of each eye, making their eyes look prominent among the other facial displays occurring (agonistic puckers, whale eye, tension in facial ridges of pup on the left.)

Notice "eye-liner" markings on both wolves: light colored patches along the eyebrow ridge (wolf on right), stripes down center of both of their muzzles. All these markings lend emphasis to varied facial, expressive displays.

Fear:

(Also see *Motivations for Behavior*)

Fear is a primary motivator of behavior, usually resulting in *submission*, flight, or a fight. If the frightened canid cannot escape from the threat he perceives from another canid, human or environmental stimulus, he is apt to respond with threats or an attack.

The five "F"s that indicate fear and stress:

- Freeze

- Fidget (or fooling around)

- Flee

- Fight

- Faint

Fear Display:

(Also see *Crouch, Ears Back, Tail Tuck, Indicators of Stress, Pinch Ear, Submission*)

Canids signal *fear* with specific postures, facial expressions, tail and ear positions.

"Every vestige of fear expresses itself in a corresponding movement of the ears and the corners of the mouth, as though the unseen powers which aid flight were pulling the dog backwards" (Konrad Lorenz, 1953, p. 56).

Fox on the left responds fearfully to the dominant posturing of the threatening fox. Note: arched back, curled body posture, ears pressed back, tail tucked between his legs.

Fearfully submissive wolf on right, demonstrates ears back, tongue flick, arched back, and tail tucked between her legs.

Feint and Parry:

Canids feint and parry during *ritualized aggression* much as humans use the same moves when *boxing* or fencing. Feinting and parrying are essential *metasignals* that identify *aggression* as ritualized *sparring*. In actual combat, the competitors would make direct, sharp moves toward each other, with intention to inflict harm.

Feint:

- *noun* a deceptive or pretended attacking movement, especially in *boxing* or fencing.
- *verb* make a feint.

Parry:

- *verb* (parries, parried) ward off (a weapon or attack) with a countermove.
- *noun* (pl. parries) an act of parrying. (AskOxford.com)

Husky-Mix on left parries to avoid attack from the Wheaton Terrier.

The submissive-aggressive wolf uses a feint – blow to the nose – to distract his wolf opponent from carrying out his attack during ritualized aggressive encounter.

Fixed Action Patterns (FAP) (Also Called Motor Patterns):

Such regular and predictable specific behaviors, which are not dependent upon learning in order to appear, are called "fixed action patterns." When we genetically manipulate *aggression* in a dog breed we are making a quantitative, not a qualitative, change. We do not alter the basic behavior patterns, but rather their likelihood and how easily they can be triggered in the dog (Coren, 2004, p. 131).

Predation is the most obvious FAP in Canids. Canids can vary the action patterns by using different behaviors for the *kill bite*. Some dogs add the *kill shake* to the grab bite during the "kill" phase, and even young puppies can be seen practicing *kill shakes*.

"The pattern varies somewhat from breed to breed, with elements of the pattern having hypertrophied (become stronger) in some breeds ("giving eye" in the border Collie) while others such as hounds do not '*give eye*' at all" (Coppinger, 2001, p. 208-211).

Bird dog trainers know they can't train a young dog until after it shows "point." Point is innate; it is wired into the dog's brain. The same is true with the border Collie, which has "eye" hardwired in. It's impossible even to try to herd sheep with a pup until it shows eye. What a border Collie handler does is train the dog when and how to go in order to use the eye. But nobody can train a dog to show eye, or to point (Coppinger, 2001, p. 19).

According to Coren, dog-to-dog *aggression* is part of a fixed action pattern:

It may seem odd, but you can manipulate behaviors more easily by using selective breeding when the behaviors are relatively complicated and multileveled. Much of the genetic programming of fundamental movements and reflex responses appears to be fixed and immutable. Thus, aggression, which is complex, has been genetically manipulated and aggressive behaviors vary widely across different breeds. Although we can increase or decrease aggressive tendencies through controlled breeding, we can't change the fact that all dog breeds fight in the same way. Their basic patterns of attack, their biting and defensive moves seem to be unalterable aspects of the basic genetic code of canines.

Coren describes fixed action patterns in epimeletic maternal-infant care-giving behaviors:

Consider care-giving behavior in mother dogs. While this complex behavior is not a fixed action pattern, a number of its major aspects are. The female dog having her first litter is pre-programmed to know what to do.... This behavior is so fixed and stereotyped that we can predict with relative certainty that the cord will be cut using a carnassial tooth (the upper tooth right before the molar). Next the puppy will be licked dry and, if necessary the umbilical cord will be trimmed shorter.... Licking is a vital fixed action pattern serving to stimulate various muscle reflexes, including those involved in breathing. It also triggers elimination behavior. Obviously if we had to teach every dog to do these things, instead of relying on genetically encoded instructions, the survival of the species would be at risk.

Coren continues:

> It is a remarkable testimony to the stability of *fixed action patterns* that even with more than fourteen thousand years of domestication, and despite concerted efforts to alter dogs genetically, so few changes have occurred in the ancestral patterns of behavior. Our genetic manipulations have only minor effects on which behaviors a dog uses, but have a strong effect on how frequently such behaviors are expressed (Coren, 2004, p. 131-132).

Coppinger describes the changes in predation-related fixed action patterns by charting how the *predation sequence* has been altered by selective breeding. These changes are most apparent when viewing the progressive changes from wolves and other wild canids to herding dogs and livestock guardian dogs.

Wolves & other wild canids	Orient	Eye	Stalk	Chase	Grab-bite	Kill-bite
Headers *(Border Collies)*	Orient	Eye	**Stalk**	**Chase**	(Grab-bite)	(Kill-bite)
LGD *(Great Pyrenees, etc)*	(Orient)	(Eye)	(Stalk)	(Chase)	(Grab-bite)	(Kill-bite)

bold = hypertrophied ( ) = fault

(chart adapted from Coppinger, 2001, p. 199)

Flooding:

(Also see *Counter Conditioning, Desensitization, Habituation, Learned Helplessness*)

Flooding is a form of *habituation*. With flooding, animals can just get used to the stimulus or they can become sensitized.

> Flooding is prolonged and forced exposure to a stimulus that is or has become unpleasant. It includes pulling a fearful dog into a swimming pool or immersing a dog-reactive dog in an environment with numerous other dogs. When the dog is flooded with the stimulus, they can "shut down" from stress and won't exhibit any of the problem behaviors. This is not fixing the behavior, although it appears to be, because the dog does not show overt signs of aggression that are recognizable by the average dog lover. This type of therapy is considered unethical in humans, as it has been known to cause trauma (Mullinax).

"Flooding is also called 'response blocking' because the animal wants to run away and the trainer is blocking that response." (Lore Haug, letter to author, July 2, 2007)

> Flooding involves prolonged exposure at a level that provokes the response so that the animal eventually gives up. This is exactly the opposite of the approach taken in desensitization. It is far more stressful than any of the other therapy strategies and, used inappropriately, could damage the animal. The most common side effect is enhanced fear. This technique should be used only by those with extensive experience and as a last resort (Merck).

Behavior modification through *desensitization* and *counter-conditioning* are far preferable and safer than flooding, and offer lasting positive changes to canine behavior.

Foreleg Stab:

(Also see *Parry*):

Foreleg stabs may be difficult to distinguish from vigorous *pawing*. *Pawing* is likely to begin with an upward motion followed by an outward motion – while the foreleg stab would emanate more from the shoulder, with an outward thrust.

Dog on the left does a foreleg stab to fend off the dog on the right. This behavior would also be considered a parry.

Dog on the right is doing a foreleg stab.

Foreleg stab misses its mark, due to evasive action on the part of the wolf on the right.

Freeze:

Freezes are moments during which a canid stops all intentional movement of voluntary muscles (i.e. they continue breathing and all other movements related to autonomic functions). A freeze may occur so quickly that it is hard to recognize, unless the observer knows the specific signs for which she should be watching. Freezes often happen in the context of play and *ritualized aggression* in the instant when the dogs make a decision between fight, flight or play.

Freezes also happen during *predatory play* sequences, when the dogs swap roles and reverse who is playing predator and who is prey.

In both dog-to-dog and dog-to-human interactions, a freeze may precede a bite. Freezes, as a precursor to aggressive or defensive bites, may be recognized as the moment when the dog closes his mouth and ceases all other active voluntary movement.

Standing Still (Freeze)

Barbara Handelman

Lynn Crook

During this freeze, the two dogs make their decision: flight, fight, or play. The metasignals conveying intent are subtle. The dog on the left does a paw-lift, while the dog in the foreground does a head turn.

Lynn Crook

Play it is!

During this freeze, Wicked does a play bow metasignal, indicating playful intentions. In the next moment, roles in the play dynamics shifted – the pursuer became the pursued.

Play after freeze.

Freezes are also part of the predation sequence. The freeze is a part of the communication between predator and prey. A wolf orients on a deer or other prey animal – the deer sees the wolf and freezes – the deer flags its tail – if the wolf holds its freeze, the deer will mirror the behavior by freezing as well. If the wolf relaxes, the deer or other prey animal will return to browsing for food. If the deer continues to flag its tail, the wolf will hold its freeze and then the deer will bound away. If, when the wolf freezes, the deer or bison does not flag, the wolf knows that he has a good chance of success in predation and will stalk and then lunge after the deer. Prey and predators often have very complex methods of communication to avoid expensive utilization of energy in predation/escape strategies (Sue Alexander, letter to author, August 15, 2007).

Two wolves freeze while testing the bison, which is flagging his tail.

Frontal Cortex:

(Also see *Limbic System*)

When the frontal cortex of the brain is engaged, canids are in a mind-set for learning. Their arousal levels are low. They are receptive to learning, and able to engage without fight or flight impulses flooding the encounter.

Functional Systems:

Behavior patterns come organized in readily identifiable "packages" called functional systems. Simply stated, there are unique behavior patterns associated in particular categories. For example, in dogs, 'play' is made up of behaviors involving chase, capture and kill – but with an inhibition to bite hard and thus do actual damage (Klinghammer, 1992, p. 4).

Any glimpse into the life of an animal quickens our own and makes it so much the larger and better in every way.

– John Muir

DOG, n. A kind of additional or subsidiary Deity designed to catch the overflow and surplus of the world's worship.
– Ambrose Bierce

Two wolves threaten each other using the gape expression.
Photo by Monty Sloan

Section 8:
Gape – Greeting Behaviors

Gape:

(Also see *Ritualized Aggression*, *Threat Behaviors*)

"Open mouth threat almost always used defensively. The lips are retracted both horizontally and vertically" (Goodman, et al., 2002, p. 11).

Lab on the left does a gape during jaw wrestling.

Two wolves express defensive, agonistic threats by using gape facial expression, in which their lips are retracted both horizontally and vertically.

Give Eye:

(Also see *Predation Sequence*)

Giving eye is the first part of the *predation* sequence. It is another name for eye stalking or orienting.

Monty Sloan

This wolf gives eye as he stalks his prey.

Greeting Behaviors:

(Also see *Affiliative Behavior*, *Hip Nudge*, *Head Press*, *Rally*)

Canids have myriad ways of greeting each other:

> Examples: Touching and *sniffing* each other's noses, *inguinal sniffs, butt sniffs*, are among the most common. Canids may use the same greeting behaviors when meeting members of other species. On-lead greetings differ from the greeting behaviors of dogs who are free to move around at will. Some dogs experience increased arousal that may easily escalate to *aggression* when on-lead. On-lead *Aggression* is a form of *barrier frustration* or *barrier aggression.*

Barbara Handelman

The three dogs in this group know each other well; only the golden is new to the group. She is being inspected fore and aft with butt sniff, inguinal sniff, and face to face greetings all happening at the same time. Notice that the dogs are all wagging their tails, and appear generally relaxed.

Barbara Handelman

These two dogs have played together on a number of occasions, always maintaining some degree of tension and reservation. The intact Collie often makes sexual advances, which Louie, the white dog, does not appreciate. While their tension has never tipped over into an attack, they are wary of each other. They are circling with their bodies both forming C-curves, distance increasing postures.

Jennifer Parizo

Inter-species greeting: this was Pan's first encounter with a horse. He used a muzzle nudge to the horse's mouth, much as he would greet a large unfamiliar dog.

111

Barbara Handelman

Nose-to-nose inter-species greetings.

Debi Davis

Peek, the service dog, and Charlie, the Maine Coon cat, are housemates, greeting nose-to-nose.

Monty Sloan

Coyote pups greet with a soft muzzle grab.

Monty Sloan

Adult wolves do a soft muzzle grab as an affiliative gesture during greeting.

Barbara Handelman

Puppy's first encounter with himself in the mirror – very curious greeting!

Barbara Handelman

On-leash greeting behavior. Dogs would like to circle each other. Border Collie is very stiff. He offers an exaggerated paw-lift. The dramatic paw-lift may warn of oncoming aggression. On-lead greetings should be kept short and repeated after short separations – rather than allowing the dogs to linger and tensions to build.

Wolf on the left does a hip slam powerful enough to knock the other wolf off his feet, but misses. Despite being on a slick, icy lake surface, the wolf on the right seems to have evaded the slam. He offers an agonistic pucker to express his submissive-aggression, and active submissive postures (tail tucked, head lowered, and ears back) all at the same time.

Photo by Monty Sloan

Section 9:
Habituation – Hip Slam

Habituation:

(Also see *Learning Theory*)

Habituation occurs only in the absence of negative consequences.

> Habituation is the outcome of repeated exposures to a stimulus until the learner ceases to respond to that stimulus. For example, when the refrigerator motor comes on a dog may initially startle, but after time will cease to respond to that particular motor as a stimulus. Cessation of response is the result of the stimulus having no value to the animal, either as a cue, a reward, or a punishment (Sue Alexander, letter to author, August, 2007).

The doorbell in my home rings many times a day, announcing the arrival of clients to our basement office. My three dogs do not respond to the doorbell in any way. The bell portends nothing exciting to them. The clients enter a part of the house into which the dogs never go. The dogs do not anticipate an opportunity to greet new arrivals. Each of my dogs grew up with these conditions. If I were to bring a new, adult dog into the house, who had previously learned that doorbells are harbingers of exciting events, that dog would undoubtedly bark at the sound of the bell. The fact that the resident dogs do not respond might help to habituate a new dog to the meaningless sounding of the doorbell. More likely, my dogs would learn to bark along with the new dog – because arousal begets arousal and the barking becomes *allelomimetic behavior*.

Hackles:

(See *Piloerector Reflex*)

Head Lowered:

To interpret the meaning of a dog's lowered head, particular attention needs to be paid to the context. Most often head lowering is a sign of *stress, submission* or *appeasement*. However, some dogs also lower their shoulders and head simultaneously when beginning to stalk prey.

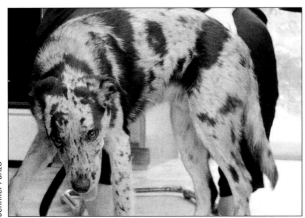

Dog has lowered his head as a sign of extreme stress.

Dog on left has lowered his head submissively.

Head Press:

(Also see *Reproductive/Courtship Behavior*)

A head press occurs when two animals press a portion of their face or head against the side of another animal's head.

It is not entirely clear what canids intend when they use the head press behavior, but it is clear that the gesture is both offered and received with gentleness. The head press can be seen during courtship/mating behaviors, but the head press is not used exclusively in that context.

Barbara Handelman

Louie, adult dog on left, does head press with puppy, Lear, his housemate. This appears to be an affectionate gesture.

Barbara Handelman

Pan, the Collie pup, presses his head against Louie's head. This, too, appears to be a gesture of affiliative affection.

Monty Sloan

Two wolves engage in an affectionate moment while doing a head press.

Barbara Handelman

This is the first meeting between Scout, the Greyhound, and Puck, the cat. They are doing a head press, after a succession of other greeting behaviors had already occurred.

Head Tilt:

The canid who tilts or cocks his head to one side is usually expressing curiosity about a new sound, sight, or smell in the environment.

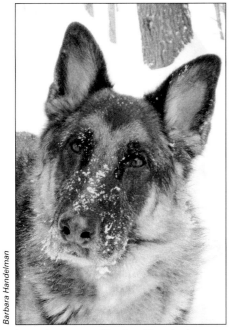

Luca, the German Shepherd Dog, looks up when spoken to, and does a head tilt, as if it will aide his understanding.

Anna, the Greyhound, does a head tilt out of curiosity about words being spoken to her.

Wolf does head tilt out of curiosity.

Head Turn:

A head turn is a *displacement signal* or a *distance increasing behavior*. It conveys that the dog doing the head turn wishes to distance himself from activity nearby. May be accompanied by: averted eyes, *paw-lift, tongue flicks,* and other *distance increasing behaviors.*

Inter species head turns – both the dog and the cat are offering signals that they intend no harm. Dog is also blinking, to emphasize his peaceful intentions.

These two dogs met head on and immediately did head turns to diffuse the tension that might arise from such a direct meeting.

Great Dane puppy is playing with wolf pups of similar age. He offers both a head turn and a paw-lift to his playmates.

Wolf on the right has turned his head away, averted his eyes and lifted his paw, as appeasement signals to the lying-down wolf, who is making challenging direct eye contact.

Head Turn with Body Turn-Away:

(Also see *Distance Increasing Signals*)

A more extreme version of the head turn, which includes turning of the canid's neck and shoulders away from the activity with which he is uncomfortable.

Dog in the background does an exaggerated tongue flick and a head turn also rotating his shoulders away from the baby Pit Bull. Although only ten-weeks-old, the Pit Bull is consistently successful in guarding food. Her ten-month-old housemate wants to avoid conflict and thus does an exaggerated head and shoulder turn away, to convey his lack of intention to compete.

Height Seeking:

(Also see *Rearing, Standing Tall, Testing*)

Height seeking is a behavior used offensively, in both canid-to-canid and canid-to-human interactions. It may occur because canids want to make themselves seem larger than an opponent, or to declare sexual rights over another animal. Canids may seek a high perch such as furniture or tree trunks to obtain the tactical advantage of height during mock or real fights.

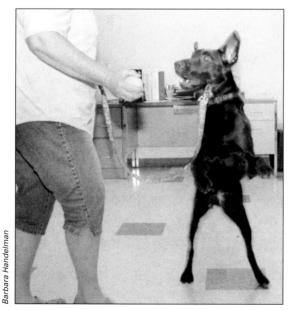

This dog is using height seeking in the form of rearing. He looks like he might simply be focused on the ball with the desire to play interactively. In fact, the dog was challenging the person who held the ball. During this evaluation session, he displayed no interest in interacting. He wanted what he wanted, when he wanted it. He was barking incessantly and insistently while pawing the air. His rearing created more proximity to human eye level and increased the threat he posed.

119

Barbara Handelman

Wolf standing on a log, uses height advantage to keep other wolves from gaining access to the treat near his front feet.

Monty Sloan

Wolf seeks out the highest vantage from which to protect his prize from other wolves.

Herding:

(Also see *Predation*)

Herding behaviors are *fixed action patterns* that have been modified over generations of selective breeding to include the functional aspects of predatory behavior, orienting, stalking, and chasing – but stop short of bite, kill and consume.

Some dogs have been selectively bred as "headers" for their ability to work, at a distance from and usually facing the stock, with intense eying, stalking, and gathering abilities (Border Collies).

Others have been selectively bred as "heelers" to work from behind the stock, nipping at their heels and following closely in order to move the stock from place to place (Corgis).

Other breeds use different combinations of heading and heeling behaviors with different aspects of the *fixed action patterns* contributing to their behaviors depending on the type of stock they work, the terrain they must cover, and the need to work with greater or lesser direction from a human handler.

This Border Collie is driving a group of sheep towards the shepherd. Note that she stays well back from the flock, using measured pressure from her "eye" and stalking posture to keep them moving.

This Border Collie and shepherd together work a very large flock. The dog is on one side, able to swing in either direction to turn any sheep that attempts to break from the flock. The shepherd works from the far side of the flock, opposite her dog.

121

Heterochrony:

(Also see *Domestication, Neoteny, Ontogeny,* and *Paedomorphosis*)

"A change in the timing of rate of developmental events, relative to the same events in the ancestor" (Goodwin et al., 1996, p. 297).

The concordance of morphological and behavioral features found in the domestic dog is best explained by the evolutionary mechanism of heterochrony (Serpell, 1995, p. 43).

Heterochrony is the mechanism that controls the rate of growth, of both physical structures and behavioral characteristics.

Domestic dogs and their wolf ancestors have identical gestation periods (60-64 days). All canine species and breeds (with the exception of the Borzoi), are born with the same face shape, which facilitates nursing. The rate of growth of physical structures and the rate of development of species or breed characteristics is call heterochrony, and accounts for the great divergence of dog appearance and behavioral traits.

Can one change size without changing shape (isometric growth)? Puppies have a highly adaptive shape for suckling. As they grow, they must change shape (allometric growth) to the adaptive adult shape. The allometic and isometric grow differences of coyotes and wolves are exactly what is going on with the different breeds of dogs....

All the different shapes of dog skulls can be explained by slight difference in the onset and rate of development, resulting often in just tiny size differences in the paired nasal bones.

The breed differences in adult dog behaviors are timing differences (heterochrony) in the onsets, offset, and rates of growth among breeds....

There are limits to how much the timings can be changed. The extreme faces of the bulldog and the Borzoi are perhaps the limits of what is possible. These breeds might not be able to survive any additional selection for shorter or longer faces. There are developmental restraints beyond which no animal can survive (Coppinger, 2001, p. 300-302).

Hip Nudge Greeting:

(Also see *Affiliative Behavior, Greeting Behaviors*)

The hip nudge is a form of friendly greeting. Dogs turn their backs to other dogs or people and bump them with their hips or butt as a way to express that they are enthusiastically *affiliative*.

This Lab is doing a hip nudge. He has backed up against my leg and is alternately leaning and bumping against me.

Jennifer Parizo

Hip Slams:

The hip slam, also called "rump bumping," may be part of a play interaction or a true fight. When a canid does a hip slam he pivots on his forepaws and slams into his target with his back end. Depending on his intent, the slam may be hard enough to knock the targeted animal off his feet.

Jennifer Parizo

Rough puppy play includes a hip slam by both puppies in this interaction. They are both also offering metasignals that make clear that this interaction is strictly play. Puppy on left does a paw-lift. The puppy on the right is blinking and doing a head turn.

Monty Sloan

Wolf in the center hip slams the wolf on the left, knocking both the wolf on his right and the wolf on his left off balance.

Puppy engaged in investigatory behavior, sniffing the flower.

Photo by Barbara Handelman

Section 10:
Infantile – Investigatory Behavior

Infantile or Neonatal Behavior:

(Also see *Et-Epimeletic Behavior*)

Infantile and neonatal behaviors include all behaviors that occur during the infant stage including: sucking, kneading with alternating front feet, pushing with outstretched hind feet, hip twist, heat seeking, etc.

Occasionally infantile or neonatal behavior occurs in adult dogs, in the form of: wool sucking, kneading, or frogging their legs behind them as they sleep.

Jennifer Parizo

These pups, only a few days old, are crawling toward their littermates, guided by heat sensing ability and smell. They cuddle up to the warmth of their mother and/or littermates.

Ingestive Behavior:

"Any behaviour involved with the procurement, consumption, and storage of food" (Sue Alexander, letter to author, August, 2007).

Digging is an ingestive behavior in dogs bred to hunt for prey by *digging* such as the Dachshund, and many terriers. (Eating, tasting foreign or non-food items – might also fall under *investigatory behavior*) (Scott and Fuller, 1965, p. 72).

Drinking is an ingestive behavior. Canids have different styles of drinking – most commonly they lap water with their tongues. Some like to take a bite of water as if it were solid matter, and swallow what they can, as the rest runs out the front and sides of their mouths. As a young dog, Luca's favorite thing was to run past his water bowl and grab a mouthful of water without stopping; he would leave a trail of small puddles as he continued on his way.

Additional ingestive behaviors are illustrated in the photographs on the next page.

Barbara Handelman

Puppies use their front feet to press and kneed the mother's teats, and cause her milk to let down so that they can feed.

Barbara Handelman

Sucking, pushing with head, alternately pushing with forepaws, hind feet pushing, tail out and down.

Barbara Handelman

Lapping, tail out and down.

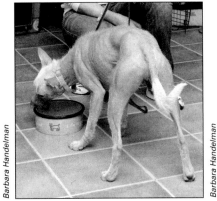

Barbara Handelman

Chewing and swallowing, tail out and down

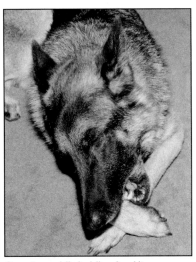

Barbara Handelman

Gnawing, while holding food-item or chew toy with paws.

Monty Sloan

A wolf laps up a drink while standing in a pond.

Barbara Handelman

Pan laps up a drink of water while standing in a lake.

Monty Sloan

This wolf has an unusual mode of drinking, she takes a bite of water from the surface of the pond.

Inguinal:

(Also see *Anatomy*)

"The inguinal region of the abdomen only includes the 'groin' area (lateral aspect of the abdomen near the angle of the thighs) and does not include the central part where the prepuce would lie. Nor does it include the vulva or scrotum. The genitalia would not fall in this area in either sex" (Lore Haug, letter to author, June 17, 2007).

Inguinal Display (Also Called Twist Movement):

The twist movement is a behavioral display, signifying submissive vulnerability. An adult dog while standing, sitting or lying on his back, can do the twist movement.

When first born, puppies are unable to eliminate independently. The mother dog must lick the pups' genitals and anus to stimulate urination and defecation. As the puppies mature, their bodies function without the maternal stimulation. The outward movement of the hip, that exposes the puppy's genital and inguinal areas, is retained into adulthood as a submissive display of vulnerability.

When seen in older puppies or adult canids, the behavior is triggered by the animal or human towards whom it is directed

Puppy does hip twist, also called inguinal display, to enable mother to lick his genitals so that he can defecate and urinate.

Puppy does inguinal display as he submissively turns on his side.

Passively submissive wolf does an inguinal display, and tongue flick as the wolf who is dominant in this interaction stands over him.

127

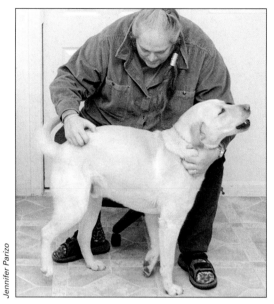

Jennifer Parizo

Actively submissive Lab does an inguinal twist while standing – he has rotated his right rear leg outward. He is also doing a paw-lift and wagging his tail while he gets his butt scratched.

Inguinal Sniffs:

Inguinal sniffs, commonly called "groin sniffs", rival *butt sniff*s as the most common form of dog-to-dog greeting.

Barbara Handelman

Inguinal sniffs are both greeting behaviors and investigatory behaviors, as the sniffing dog gathers information about the other dog.

Marco De Kloet

Dog's eye view of an inguinal sniff.

Instinct:

An instinct is a behavior that appears in its fully functional form the first time it is performed. The instinctive behavior usually requires a mechanical trigger to set the behavior in motion for the first time.

Some instinctive behaviors are evoked by specific environmental events or a simple cue in the form of a sight, sound or smell. Instinctive behaviors include inherited breed characteristics such as "eye" in a Border Collie, or "pointing" in hunting dogs. Learning and environmental factors play a role in refining instinctive behaviors. E.g., without training, Border Collies may not have fully functional heading ability or herding ability but they may have "eye" immediately.

Puppies' instinctive behaviors – during the neonatal period – include finding warmth from their littermates' or mother's bodies; recognizing the smell of milk, moving toward a teat, and suckling.

Barbara Handelman

This Border Collie uses movement, posture, and his powerful instinctive stare or "eye" to turn the flock of sheep.

iStockphoto/Margo Harrison

Two border Collies work to herd a small group of sheep. While herding, dogs are apt to be aroused by the actions of their canine co-workers. Working well as a team requires that each dog have exquisite self-control and a high level of training.

iStockphoto /Kate Leigh

The Border Collie's predatory instinct to chase, has been modified to become part of the herding fixed action pattern, to chase and circle a flock in order to stop the sheep's movement or change the direction of their movement.

Investigatory Behavior:

"Any behaviour where the canid gathers sensory information about his environment" (Sue Alexander, letter to author, August, 2007).

- Running with nose to the ground, *sniffing*.
- Head in the air, *sniffing*, may run from side to side.
- *Sniffing* anal and/or genital region.
- *Sniffing* nose to face.
- Nosing or *sniffing* urine or feces.
- Crawling forward, moving head from side to side, *sniffing* (Scott and Fuller, 1965, p. 78).

These two dogs are sniffing the ground. This may be investigatory behavior, or it may be displacement behavior in which sniffing serves to slow down play, before arousal levels heighten and tip over into aggression.

Boxer is checking out the "pee mail", gathering information from the urine signature of a previous canine passerby.

For this young Great Pyrenees puppy, sniffing while cruising a new environment is a fixed action pattern.

This Terrier is gathering information by air scenting.

Jaw Punch:

(See *Muzzle Punch*)

Jaw Wrestling (Also Called Jaw Sparring):

(Also see *Ritualized Aggression*)

Canids use their open jaws to spar with each other as if they are fencing. They *feint* and *parry* just as human fencers might, but neither participant closes his mouth with force and no injuries occur.

These two-week-old puppies are jaw wrestling even before they can walk. Pups from this litter were also videotaped jaw sparring at 8-days-of-age before their eyes had opened.

Young Coyote puppies, three- or four-months old, jaw wrestling.

Two young wolf puppies make the ugliest, most threatening faces they can muster while jaw wrestling.

Jaw wrestling wolves, both with wide gape displays. This is ritualized aggression.

131

Lateral Display (Also Called "Broadside Display" in other species):

(Also see *Standing Tall*)

"One animal stands broadside to another, standing tall, head up, ears pricked, tail level with back or raised over the back, with some piloerection; it may try to challenge the other canid by forcing eye contact" (Goodman, et al., 2002, p. 18).

"The advantage to a lateral display over a frontal display is that more of the body may be seen and thus more information may be communicated" (Sue Alexander, personal communication, August, 2007).

Two wolves engaged in lateral displays: both show piloerection – wolf in the foreground's tail is very fluffed out as part of his display. They are challenging each other to make eye-contact.

Lateral display in which wolf on the right appears to be threatening the wolf on the left – who is offering a quick tongue flick, and paw-lift. Both wolves display mild piloerection.

Beau had had a proper drink of tap water before we started from home, but this drink was different. I could tell from the varied, eager, slurping sounds that emanated from Beau. He was intoxicated by living water which dim primordial memories had instructed him how to secure.

– Loren Eiseley

Pan is learning to target the buttons on the toy.

Photo by Jennifer Parizo

Section 11:
Learning Theory Terminology and Methodology

(Also see *Allelomimetic Behavior, Flooding, Habituation, and Social Facilitation*)

Learning:

The act of acquiring new information, understanding or skills that leads to modification of attitudes, emotions, or behaviors.

An understanding of learning theory is important for all dog professionals. Learning theory is science-based and produces strategies that can solve canine behavior problems and teach myriad new behaviors. Learning theory is applicable to all species, including humans. The following is an overview of learning theory terminology and methodology:

The Stages of Learning:

It is useful to think of learning as a sequence of three stages:

1. **Acquisition:** Acquiring – learning a new behavior

   The behavior may be learned through *targeting, luring, modeling, capturing* or *shaping*.

2. **Generalization:** On the way to fluency

   Applying *The Five "D"s* (see page 148)

3. **Fluency** (automatic): The animal performs the behavior, on cue, in a wide variety of situations – responding correctly to the cue at least 80% of the time.

Cues, Prompts, Reinforcements, Responses, Rewards and Stimuli

Cues:

Cues are signals, words or other stimuli that reliably result in the animal performing a particular behavior.

Prompts:

Prompts are actions performed – usually without intention – by the trainer, that guide the dog toward completion of the behavior. Unlike cues – which are specific and intentional – prompts are inconsistent and variable. The dog becomes accustomed to a prompt and may wait for it to occur before performing the cued behavior.

> Example: Many trainers lean forward while calling their dogs. Leaning forward is a prompt.

---

1 The author gratefully acknowledges the contributions of Dee Ganley, Debi Davis, Melissa Alexander, Sue Alexander and Lore Haug for their generous contributions to this section of the book.

Reinforcement (R):

Something the learner desires that happens immediately after the behavior – which causes the dog to be more likely to repeat that behavior in the future.

Examples: food, toys, going for a walk. A reinforcer must be something the animal actually wants – not something a person thinks the dog wants.

Primary Reinforcer:

Primary reinforcers are things needed for survival, and therefore have inherent reward value.

Examples:

- Food
- Chasing prey
- Water
- Social contact (for social species)
- Shelter

Secondary Reinforcer (conditioned reinforcer or bridging stimulus):

A stimulus that attains reward value (through *classical conditioning*) by being paired with a primary reinforcer. It can be used to "mark" the desired goal behavior.

Examples: verbal praise or the sound of a clicker.

Unconditioned Response:

An unconditioned response is the natural reflexive reaction to a stimulus.

Examples:

- Salivation
- Eye blink
- Increased respiration rate

The Premack Principle:

Behavioral psychologist, David Premack, discovered that one could increase the frequency of a low probability behavior by making it the contingency for a higher probability behavior. This rule is called the Premack Principle.

Some examples of Premack are:

- "As soon as you finish your homework – you may go play outside."
- "Eat your vegetables – then you can have dessert."

Rewards (Reinforcers):

Anything that the dog perceives as rewarding at that time – items that are rewarding for one dog may not be rewarding for another. What is rewarding in the dog's home may not be sufficiently rewarding to motivate the dog when out on the street.

Examples: yummy treats, roast beef, turkey, cheese, toys and balls for playing, freedom to check out the environment, freedom to play with another dog.

Unconditioned Stimulus:

An unconditioned stimulus is the natural trigger for a particular behavior. Example: the smell of food is an unconditioned stimulus for drooling (salivation).

Conditioned Stimulus:

A neutral stimulus that has become associated with an unconditioned stimulus and now produces the same response.

> Example: The bell in Pavlov's experiment was rung before food was presented and became associated with food. Later, the dog drooled when hearing the bell ring. The bell became a conditioned stimulus for drooling.

Event Marker (secondary or conditioned reinforcer):

An event marker is a stimulus (usually a sound or short word) with which the trainer marks the exact moment when the animal performs the desired behavior. Many trainers use clickers, whistles, or other mechanical devices with which they can mark the behavior precisely and with the exact same sound each and every time the behavior is offered. The human voice – even saying a one-syllable word such as "yes" – can vary with inflection, loudness and attitude that unintentionally accompany the marker word. The human voice is, therefore, less precise than a clicker or whistle. Mechanical devices give the trainer the precision of a scalpel with which to mark the animal's behavior. Because of the accuracy of the marker, the animal can discern precisely which fragment of a behavior is being rewarded.

Fluency:

(Also see *The Five "D"s*):

Fluency is the ability to do the behavior immediately after the cue is given. A behavior cannot be said to be fluent, or under stimulus control, until it is consistent 80% of the time – and the animal performs the behavior regardless of distractions.

Barbara Handelman

Pan has achieved fluency with a foot targeting exercise in which he presses an "Easy Button" that is on top of a ladder.

Operant Conditioning:

Operant Conditioning is a term first coined by B.F. Skinner and his colleague Fred Keller in the late 1920s. Keller and Marian Breland, and Robert Bailey later applied operant conditioning to the training of marine mammals, dogs, and other animals. Karen Pryor was the first to bring the theories of behaviorism – including operant conditioning – to popular light in the dog world in her 1985 book, *Don't Shoot the Dog*.

Operant Conditioning is an analytical response to cause and effect. Operant conditioning involves thinking and reasoning to associate a behavior with its consequences. The consequence of a behavior can be positive or *negative reinforcement*, or positive or *negative punishment*. An animal with free choice learns which behavior results in which consequence. Thus, he is most likely to perform behaviors that offer the most reinforcing and the least punishing consequences.

> Example: A handler reinforces the dog with food each time the dog sits. He always ignores the dog for jumping up. The dog is most likely to sit rather than jump up, in the context of greeting the handler. This exercise is the first step in building a "default sit". In order for the sit-for-greeting to become the dog's "default" behavior, the exercise would need to be practiced with many people, in many situations and under the challenge of all *five "D"s*.

The Five Segments of Operant Conditioning:
- *Positive Reinforcement*
- *Negative Reinforcement*
- *Positive Punishment*
- *Negative Punishment*
- *Extinction.*

All five are part of *operant conditioning*. "Clicker trainers" rely mostly, but not exclusively, on *positive reinforcement.*

Positive Reinforcement (R+):
The addition of a stimulus concurrent with or immediately after the target behavior enhances the probability that the behavior will increase in frequency in the future. In other words, the trainer gives the dog something it desires (such as food, play, praise) after performance of the behavior.

> Example: A handler reinforces the dog with food each time the dog sits. He always ignores the dog for jumping up. The dog is most likely to sit rather than jump up, in the context of greeting the handler.

Positive reinforcement training helps animals learn how to learn. It promotes enjoyment of the learning process, comfort with trying or offering new behaviors, and a willingness to risk making mistakes.

Negative Reinforcement (R-):
An aversive stimulus is removed concurrent with or immediately after the target behavior such that the target behavior increases in frequency in the future. In other words, something the dog wishes to avoid (such as pain or pressure) ends or is taken away.

Example: pressing on the dog's lower back to elicit a sit. When the dog sits, the pressure is released and the dog experiences relief. The feeling of relief reinforces the sit.

Positive Punishment (P+):

An aversive stimulus is added concurrent with or immediately after the target behavior such that the behavior is less likely to occur in the future.

Examples:

- The dog jumps up and gets a knee in the chest.

- A dog barks and gets sprayed with water in its face.

Negative Punishment (P-):

A stimulus is removed concurrent with or immediately after the behavior such that the behavior is less likely to occur in the future. That is, something desirable ends or is taken away.

Example: a favorite toy goes back into the person's pocket when the dog grabs for it roughly.

Schedules of Reinforcement:

When you start reinforcing behaviors you reinforce on a one-to-one (1:1) ratio. This one behavior earns one click (and one treat). This is called *continuous reinforcement* (italics theirs). The initial purpose of this type of reinforcement is simply to establish for the dog what the desired behavior is.

> ...Another way to proceed is to put the behavior on a *variable reinforcement* (italics theirs) schedule (or a variable ratio). That is, instead of 1:1 reinforcement, you will go to 2:1, 3:1, 4:1 or higher. Theoretically, you can extend the ratio of behaviors to reinforcement indefinitely.

> ....you are always 'pushing the envelope' – looking to get more of a behavior without suppressing or extinguishing the behavior (Spector, 1995, p.25).

Extinction:

A basic principle of learning theory is that behaviors that are reinforced tend to continue, and behaviors that are not reinforced tend to disappear or undergo extinction. Sometimes you can stop an unwanted behavior simply by not responding to (reinforcing) it.

Extinction Burst:

> An important corollary to the idea of extinction is extinction burst. That is, a behavior that is resistant to extinction will intensify in the absence of reinforcement before undergoing extinction. Sticking with the example of the (ball point) pen, if it has written before after a shake or two and now stops writing, you'll shake it as you did before and if it still doesn't write you'll shake it harder. This is an extinction burst (Spector, 1995, p.25).

Stimulus Control:

A behavior may be considered under stimulus control when the dog responds consistently to the cue to perform the behavior, and does not offer the behavior unless cued to do so.

Conditioned Responses

Classical Conditioning:

Associating a neutral stimulus with an unconditioned stimulus will eventually lead to the neutral stimulus producing the same response. At this point, the neutral stimulus is called a conditioned stimulus.

Classical conditioning refers to the conditioning of reflexes (e.g. salivation, eye blink) and emotions (such as *fear*).

Classically conditioned responses may override operantly conditioned responses.

Example: Noises associated with frightening events can evoke *fear*. The *fear* may cause the dog to temporarily refuse to perform an operantly conditioned response, such as sit – because emotional responses typically override cognitive ones.

Classical and operant conditioning work together, because classical associations are made during operant conditioning.

Example: "Clicker training" relies on the classical conditioning of an event marker. The clicker, or other event marker, always precedes the delivery of a reward. The event marker becomes a classically conditioned association with a food treat or other highly valued reward. Classical conditioning is a powerful tool. It usually operates on involuntary responses (e.g. salivation in anticipation of desired treat). Because it is so powerful, classical conditioning can be used to help a dog overcome *fear* and *aggression* (see counter-conditioning).

Counter Conditioning:

Pairing one stimulus that evokes a specific emotional response with another stimulus that creates an opposite emotional response, so that the first stimulus eventually evokes the second response.

Example: Luca hated having his toenails cut. He associated the nail clippers with discomfort, and responded with avoidance, or growling and snapping when the clippers were presented. For years, he was muzzled during nail clipping. Luca was introduced to the Manners Minder® (a treat dispensing machine) to which he has access only while having his nails clipped. He associates the machine, and the steady stream of high value treats it dispenses, with nail clipping and begins looking forward to having his nails clipped.

Luca turns his head and averts his eyes – avoidance behaviors that preceded growling, snarling and muzzle punches.

Luca watches the Manners Minder machine intently, waiting for it to dispense his next treat, while he ignores having his nails trimmed.

In this example, counter conditioning has occurred because the conditioned pleasure response connected to the Manners Minder® is more powerful than the association of discomfort connected to the nail clipper.

Training Outcomes

Single Stage Behaviors:

Examples:

- Sit
- Down
- Stand

Behavior Chains or Multi-Stage Behaviors:

A behavior chain is a collection of trained behaviors performed in succession.

Retrieving balls, Frisbees® and other toys is a game in which the dog and handler engage together – oftentimes with little or no training. Some dogs' eagerness to play fetch relates to their *breed-specific action patterns* (e.g. retrievers bred to find and return birds that have been shot during flight; *herding* dogs bred to chase, but not kill, livestock).

The working retrieve, on the other hand, is a complex behavior chain consisting of component behaviors initially trained separately and then combined to occur in a sequence or behavior chain.

Note: when using this method, called "The Marriage of Target and Retrieve" (see unpublished article by Barbara Handelman) hand *targeting* – with firm pressure of the dog's nose to the person's hand – is a prerequisite to accurate and consistent delivery of the retrieved object.

- Take object.
- Hold object – for increasing increments of time.
- Release object to hand – on cue.
- Fetch object placed or thrown.
- Return with object in mouth.
- Place object firmly in handler's hand.
- Release object on cue.

All photos this page: Jennifer Parizo

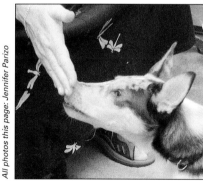

Pan, 4 months old, demonstrates targeting my hand with his nose. At this stage in training, his touch is quick.

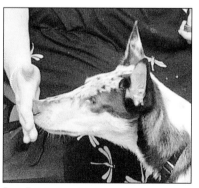

Pan, 5 months old, demonstrates a briefly sustained firm nose touch to my hand.

Pan, 8 months old, practices duration by resting his chin in my palm.

Pan, 15 months old, demonstrates a sustained touch to my palm with sufficient pressure to compress his nasal plane. He is ready now to press retrieved objects into my palm – thus marrying targeting with retrieving.

All photos this page: Jennifer Parizo

 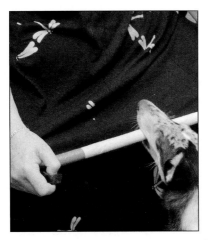 

Pan learns to "take" and "hold" by grabbing onto the "grab stick". At this stage, I do not relinquish my hold on the stick. Pan is clicked and treated for developing a progressively strong and sustained grip on the stick. By holding onto the stick, I not only can feel the strength of his grip, but I can also click him while he retains his hold.

 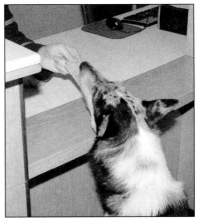

Picking up money from the ground.   Taking a hospital card from a receptionist.

Pan holds a dumbbell firmly in his mouth.   Proofing the hold by touching Pan's ears and his chest, while he retains his hold on the dumbbell.

All photos this page: Jennifer Parizo

Pan takes money from me and holds it...

... he carries it to the vendor whom I am paying...

... and he releases the money into her hand.

Pan picks up his dropped leash.

Pan holds the leash firmly.

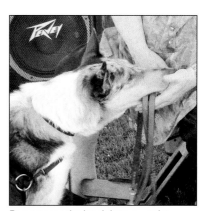

Pan presses the leash into my palm.

Pan releases the leash into my hand on cue.

143

Desensitization:

Controlled, gradual exposure to an incrementally increased noxious stimulus, produces an alternate emotional response to the stimulus. The stimulus has no consequence; therefore the dog ceases to respond to it (*habituation*).

> Example: A dog *fear*s traffic noise. It is first exposed to a period of low-level traffic noise. The dog's reaction gradually decreases to the point where he ignores the traffic noise – at that level. The noise level is increased by a small increment. The dog becomes desensitized to each increased level – before the level increases again. Using systematic *desensitization*, the dog may gradually become comfortable when exposed to very loud traffic noise.

Latency:

Latency is the measure of time between the person's issuance of the cue and dog's response to the cue.

Learned Helplessness:

Dogs who have been subjected to unpredictable episodes of punishment often exhibit symptoms of learned helplessness. They may stop responding altogether; appear depressed, insensitive to pain, stubborn, excessively passive or withdrawn.

Martin Seligman did the landmark studies on learned helplessness in dogs; he wrote:

> Experimental psychologists interested in learning have traditionally studied the behavior of animals and men faced with rewards and punishment that the subject could control. So, in a typical instrumental learning experiment, the subject can either make some response or refrain from making it and thereby influence the events around him. Nature, however, is not always so benign in its arrangement of the contingencies. Not only do we face events that we can control by our actions, but we also face many events about which we can do nothing at all. Such uncontrollable events can significantly debilitate organisms: they produce passivity in the face of trauma, inability to learn that responding is effective, and emotional stress in animals, and possibly depression in man (Seligman, 1972, p. 1).

Barbara Handelman

This Papillion puppy totally shut down during his temperament evaluation. He is demonstrating learned helplessness. His evaluation ended after only a very few minutes.

How Dogs Learn New Behaviors

Social Learning:

Social or observational learning refers to any form of learning where changes in behavior are dependent upon or facilitated by the presence of other animals.

> ...Social facilitation, in which the behaviour of one animal prompts the same behaviour by another animal but the behaviour already exists in the second animal's repertoire (Reid, 2007, p.123).

> Technically, allelomimetic behaviour is a subset of social facilitation. In social facilitation, the mere presence of another member of the same species can trigger the behaviour – so if one dog is in the kitchen sniffing the garbage and another dog comes in, the second dog may feel confident enough to raid the garbage even if the first dog merely smelled it and does not get into the garbage. Allelomimetic behaviour occurs when the second animal does exactly as the first animal who modelled the behaviour. So if a pigeon is in a cage and he watches another pigeon pecking a button to get a treat and then he tries to peck the button himself, that would be socially facilitated allelomimetic behaviour (Sue Alexander, letter to author, August, 2007).

Example: Pan first saw a large body of water when he was about twelve weeks old. Luca, a great fan of water in any form (he'd swim in his water bowl if he could fit), ran headlong into the lake and immediately swam after a ball. Pan followed closely on Luca's heels. Pan instantly began swimming. Swimming was clearly part of Pan's repertoire of innate abilities.

Example: During the early stages of Pan's assistance dog training, he was hesitant about walking into elevators. A familiar, older dog walked into the elevator and Pan followed his canine friend. After practicing a few times, he generalized the behavior to include all elevators, which he would enter on his own.

Molding (Also called Modeling):

Molding is physically guiding a dog to do a behavior. Molding also includes the use of physical props, such as working against a wall to force a straight heel.

Luring:

Luring is a hands-off method of guiding the dog through a behavior. Lures are usually food but may be target sticks or anything else the dog will follow. A common method of training a "sit" is for the trainer to hold food in front of the dog's nose, and then move the food up and back. As the dog's head follows the food, generally the back end will drop to the floor.

Targeting:

Targeting, at its most basic, is the behavior of touching a specified surface with a particular body part. In practice, targeting is much more flexible. Targets can be used to position an animal, to manipulate its body position, or transferred to a different surface – or used in combinations to get incredibly complex behaviors.

Capturing:

In capturing, the trainer waits for the dog to offer the behavior, then marks and rewards it.

Shaping:

Shaping is a technique of training a behavior by reinforcing successive approximations toward the goal behavior. To shape a spin, a trainer might start with marking the dog's glance to the left. Then a glance and a weight shift. Then a glance, a weight shift, and movement of a front paw, continuing until the dog is performing a complete spin.

Successive Approximations:

In training, when an animal learns a behavior in stages or steps, the process is called successive approximation. Trainers often allow learners to freely choose the steps that they wish to take towards the *terminal behavior,* rewarding only successive steps that bring the learner closer to the *terminal behavior*. This application of successive approximation is called shaping (Sue Alexander, letter to author, September 3, 2007).

Karen Pryor wrote:

Even B.F. Skinner did not start out training animals by *capturing* and *shaping* spontaneously offered behavior. Initially, he taught his laboratory animals to press levers and accomplish other tasks by making small changes in the environment: raising the height of a bar in small increments until an animal had to reach higher, or increasing the "stiffness" of a button so a pigeon learned to peck harder. This method was called successive approximation (Pryor, 2007).

Terminal Behavior:

The trainer's intended goal behavior, toward which the animal makes *successive approximations*.

Shaping is often called the "Method of Successive Approximation" because it involves reinforcing responses that are closer and closer approximations of the final desired response. The final desired response is termed the terminal behavior. Once the terminal behavior is achieved and has become fluent, only the terminal behavior is reinforced (Ron Lawrence).

Luca and the Laundry Basket:
An Exercise in Free Shaping by Successive Approximations

All photos this page: Barbara Handelman

1

2

3

4

5

Luca was already very clicker savvy before this challenge began.

The laundry basket was presented to Luca as a novel object in his environment. He was given no direction, but was allowed to explore and offer behaviors in relationship to the laundry basket. His successive approximations, during this shaping game, took place over several weeks of training with the basket. The photos are in the order in which he offered new behaviors. He was given many opportunities to repeat the behavior he offered at each stage along the way. After 5-7 consistent repetitions of the same approximation, the event marker was delayed to encourage Luca to offer a new behavior.

These photos represent the successive approximations along the way to the terminal behavior of curling his 70-pound body into a cramped space.

6

7

Why was curling up in a laundry basket important? Luca was a mobility assistance dog. He and I were preparing for our first cross-country flight together. On the airplane, he was expected to lie down in cramped quarters for many hours. Curling up in the laundry basket was eventually given the verbal cue "curl". Once the behavior was fluent, on cue, it then generalized to his curling up in tight quarters whenever cued to do so. Our first flight together was a success – for both of us.

8

Success!

The Five "D"s[2]:
Duration, Distance, Distraction, Diversity, and Difficulty

The Five "D"s help build behaviors to *fluency* and ensure that they are under *Stimulus Control*. In order for behaviors to become fluent, they must be able to withstand the test of the five "D"s. Pairing or combining multiple "D"s increases the criteria for reinforcement – i.e. increasing the level of skill the dog must perform in order to receive a reward.

Duration:

The length of time an animal sustains a behavior before hearing the click that marks the end of the behavior.

> Example: Increasing the time the dog holds a position, such as "sit" or "down", before hearing the click.

> Example: Incrementally increasing the time during which the dog holds a retrieved object before hearing the release cue.

Distance

The dog performs the behavior at a distance from the trainer, or the dog stays while the handler moves around or away from the dog.

Distraction:

Performing the behavior with environmental factors competing for the animal's attention.

> Examples: noise, movement, children playing, balls bouncing, squirrels running, food on the floor.

Diversity:

Diversity changes the circumstances under which the animal is asked to perform a behavior. It can be used to test for object and cue discrimination. Can the dog recognize cues in myriad settings and circumstances? When the context changes, the patterns to which the dog is accustomed are altered – the dog may not understand what is being asked of him without the familiar patterns in the context. If the dog falters, back up to an earlier stage in training where success was consistent and build again toward *fluency* in small, incremental steps.

The following examples suggest ways to add diversity to training:

- Change the trainer's position relative to that of the dog, or change the direction of the trainer's movement while issuing a cue.

- Introduce familiar training props into a training session, but either ignore the prop or use it in unexpected ways.

- Bring out a target stick, then cue the animal to perform a behavior in which the target stick does not play a part.

---

[2]   Stephen Rafe trademarked the concept of the 4 "D"s: duration, distance, distraction, and difficulty. The concept of "Diversity" in training for fluency was introduced by trainers Sherri Lippman, Virginia Broitman, and others.

- Present cues in a different order, or context, or with different equipment, so the animal practices responding even when the cue is unanticipated or familiar environmental cues are absent.

- Lie on the floor, hands covering your face, and give your dog a cue. Will your dog respond with minimal latency, even though diversity has been added?

Difficulty:

Difficulty increases incrementally as any of the four D's are paired or added in multiples to the process of achieving *fluency* with new behaviors. Difficulty also increases as behaviors are chained together, thus increasing the complexity of the behavior(s) the dog is expected to perform.

If I don't practice for a day, I know it. If I don't practice for two days, the critics know it. And if I don't practice for three days, the public knows it.

– Louis Armstrong

All animals except man know that the ultimate of life is to enjoy it.

– Samuel Butler

Punishers, like reinforcers, are defined by the receiver, not the giver.

– Karen Pryor

The Saluki appears to have taken flight while galloping at full speed during a lure coursing event.

Kevin Peuhkurinen

Section 12:
Lick Intention – Locomotion

Lick Intention:

(Also see *Appeasement Behaviors, Distance Increasing Behaviors, Tongue Flicks*)

An extension and flicking of the tongue between the lips; a licking motion performed at a distance too great to reach its intended target. May manifest as a single small flick or several slurps of almost the full length of the tongue (length of tongue and extension and number of repetitions will vary with context). Teeth may or may not be additionally bared (Goodman, et al., 2002, p. 19).

Lick intention may be a *distance increasing behavior*, or attempts to appease another canid or human. Lick intention, like tongue flicks, conveys a canid's uncertainty about or discomfort with a particular situation.

Jennifer Parizo

Lick intention, as display of appeasement toward the human.

Barbara Handelman

Aussie does lick intention to express discomfort with the Lab's approach to do a butt sniff.

Monty Sloan

Puppy does a lick intention as appeasement signal to adult wolf; note accompanying paw-lift.

Limbic System:

(Also see *Frontal Cortex, Anatomy*)

The portion of the brain that governs emotional responses.

> In the complicated circuitry of the brain, scientists have discovered an inverse relationship between activation of the cortex and activation of the limbic system. When one is activated, the other is inhibited. A dog or person who is in the grips of a strong emotion (i.e., the fight or flight response is activated) literally cannot think straight. This is not necessarily a conscious choice, but a neurochemical reality (Clothier, 1996, p. 25).

Brenda Aloff (2005, p. 11) describes the reactive dog as functioning with his "hind brain". The canid functioning in fight-or-flight mode cannot learn.

Efforts to train when either the canid or the handler are in a highly aroused state are futile and potentially risky. Either might redirect frustration or *Aggression*. The trainer may get bitten or the dog punished, without conscious intention or regard for fairness.

Lip Licking:

(Also see *Lick Intention, Tongue Flick*)

Lip licking is often a or appeasement signal one canid uses to let others know he means no harm. Lip licking is the "canid equivalent to human fidgeting" (Goodman, Motter, Wolf Park Behavior Seminar, 2007).

Monty Sloan

Two wolves do dramatic lip licking displays, which might also be considered examples of lick intention

Locomotion

• noun: movement or the ability to move from one place to another.

– ORIGIN from Latin *loco* 'from a place' + *motio* 'motion' (Oxford Dictionary Online).

Crawl:

Eleven-day-old puppies are blind and deaf, but able to perceive changes of temperature. They crawl determinedly until they are in physical contact with each other. Only then do they rest. At this age, they crawl like inchworms.

At nineteen-days, the puppies' eyes and ears are open and they can lift their weight onto their front legs and move forward, driven by their hind feet.

Amble:

To *w alk* at a leisurely pace, slowly, unhurried.

This English Setter is ambling around the dog park.

Walk:

The walk is a four beat gait, where three feet are on the ground at all times.

Trot:

The trot is two-beat gait. Only two feet are on the ground at any time. The legs on opposing sides move forward and backward at the same time: left hind, right front; right hind, left front.

This is the same Husky that is walking in the previous photo. Here he is doing a trot with lots of extension of the non-weight bearing legs.

Wolf trotting. His extended reach with the non-weight bearing legs suggests effortless speed.

Canter:

The canter is a three beat gait. One foot is always on the ground in this order: left front foot, right hind foot, right front foot, left hind foot.

Two dogs canter during a game of chase.

Pace:

When pacing both legs on one side are moving forward while both legs on the opposite side are moving backwards. Like the *trot*, pacing is also a two-beat gait with only two feet touching the ground at one time.

Renki paces as he moves through the snow. Renki receives treatment for a recurring orthopedic problem. Pacing in canids is often a telltale sign that they are experiencing pain in one or more of their legs.

Gallop:

The gallop is the canid's fastest gait, though usually not sustained over long distances. Their fast, elongated *trot* is used for long distance travel. Note how, when galloping, all four legs seem to work in unison resulting in fleeting moments when no feet are in contact with the ground. As with the canter, the sequence of feet in contact with the ground is: left front foot, right hind foot, right front foot, left hind foot.

Marco De Kloet

In this composite photo of Wicked running on a beach, it is easy to see how each foot has its brief moment on the ground in succession with the other three feet.

Accelerate:

Marco De Kloet

Wicked demonstrates his powerful ability to accelerate while making a turn.

Leap Away:

Monty Sloan

The wolf in the foreground is leaping away from the wolf in the background who has lunged toward him.

Leap Off:

Marco De Kloet

Wicked leaps off a sand dune cliff. Something has captured his attention.

Leap Up:

Monty Sloan

The wolf does a vertical leap straight up toward a treat that was hidden in the branches of a tree.

Leap Run (Also Called Rocking Horse Style Gait)

This gait is often part of *locomotory play*.

Barbara Handelman

Bronte, the Airedale, does a leap run while playing with another dog. The leap run is a metasignal indicating playful intent.

Marco De Kloet

The leap run is a variation of the canter. In the leap run, the motion of the front of the animal is exaggerated, producing a rocking horse type of motion.

Monty Sloan

The leap run is a metasignal indicating playful intent.

Observation Leap:

In doing the observation leap, the canid stands erect to extend his line of sight.

Tristan, the alpha male, is observing activity in the distance.

Leap Attack:

A leap at or onto another canid, if accompanied by *metasignals*, may occur during a play sequence. Without *metasignals* that are apparent to the participating canids, a leap at or onto another canid would constitute an attack.

This leap attack occurred during mating season. The dominant wolf – in this case, the one with breeding rights – leapt on top of another male who was courting his mate. The leaping wolf is doing an agonistic pucker. His eyes are hard – appearing narrowed with furrowing between them. His ears are forward indicating confidence.

This leap attack appears more ritualized, perhaps even playful. Both wolves are squinty eyed, a metasignal or displacement behavior indicating ambivalence. Neither wolf is doing a serious agonistic pucker. Both of their bodies appear relatively relaxed, tails are in neutral positions.

Lunge:

Lunges occur during the predatory sequence when the canid lunges to capture his prey; or during *agonistic* aggressive encounters. During play, lunges may be preceded or followed by a *metasignal,* indicating playful intent.

Luca is lunging after his "escaping" ball. In this instance, the lunge is part of a highly charged game of fetch.

Descending Stairs:

Wicked carefully descends widely spaced, steep stairs.

Swim:

Some dogs use their tails as rudders when swimming. Dogs bred for swimming usually have tails that are thick, strong and very flexible, which helps them to move easily through water and make quick turns (Wells).

Tristan, the wolf, swimming in a leisurely manner, with his head level with the water. He does not appear to be breathing hard. He almost appears motionless, or at least to be swimming with no apparent effort.

Wolf swimming fast – note puffed out cheeks suggesting that he is breathing hard with the exertion. His head is no longer level with the water. This may be because of the added effort or because he is wanting to keep an eye on an object or animal he is pursuing,

A side view of a swimming wolf. Note that the motion is so effortless it barely disturbs the water's surface.

Spaniel is swimming toward something he is watching. His head is raised slightly above water level. The rest of his body rides smoothly just below the surface; his tail serves as a rudder to help him steer.

A wolf carrying a stick while swimming becomes much less efficient moving through the water. Holding his head high forces the rest of the body below the surface. Canids who are inexperienced or fearful of water swim in this position, even when not carrying something in their mouths.

161

Although still ritualized, this is not a gentle muzzle grab. Note that the grabbing wolf uses his paws to hold the other wolf's head in place.

Photo by Monty Sloan

Section 13:
Lumpy Whisker Bed – Muzzle Punch

Lumpy Whisker Bed:

(See *Whiskers*)

Marking Behaviors:

Any behaviour associated with communicating to other animals information about territorial boundaries, evolutionary fitness, age and health status.

Marking behaviours include the use of urine as a calling card, the placement of fecal matter, and ground scraping (Sue Alexander, letter to author, 2007).

Canids use urination to leave their 'pee mail'. They can learn a lot about animals who passed before them by *sniffing* or even licking the urine of other canids. Some canids kick their feet behind them after urinating or defecating to scatter their own scent. Marking is a means of claiming territory, which is important because canids compete for resources in the environment.

"Scent-marking is differentiated from merely urinating, by a number of criteria including: sniffing before urinating followed by directing the stream of urine at urine that is already known to be present; or at another target where there might be urine" (Bekoff, 2001, p. 78).

Barbara Handelman

Wolf marking over a food wrapper, staking his claim to its contents.

Marko De Kloet

Wicked lifts his leg high to place his urine just where he wants it. He is probably over-marking a pee-mail message left by an earlier canine passerby.

Monty Sloan

This wolf is spreading scent by kicking and scratching the ground with both front and back legs. Ground scratching is both an olfactory marking and a visual marking behavior.

163

The following description of how scent marking informs wolves is also highly relevant to pet owners seeking to understand what domestic dogs learn when they sniff the urine or feces of dogs who have marked a spot before them. Dogs depend more on humans to maintain boundaries for them than they do on territorial marking as a mode of self-defense. Dogs are, nonetheless, concerned about what animals have gone before them on a street or trail. They may have much better knowledge of what dangers lie ahead (a known canine neighborhood bully, for example).

The first line of territorial defense is to prevent conflict during which you might get hurt. Wolves adhere to this rule steadfastly. Territorial marking tells others, "Stay out!" But there are many nuances to the marking process that non-odor-oriented humans (we're visually oriented) do not appreciate. Much of the wolf's skull contains odor receptors, not only in the nose but also in the mouth. The wolf, if you will, "sees" with its nose.

To better understand what it means to "see" with your nose, Jim Garry suggests imagining your vision behaving in the same way as odor receptors. A single sniff not only tells the wolf who was here but how long ago they passed. A person would see another person, but the faintness of the image would tell the passage of time. We could look back on the trail continually seeing the person, the image would get fainter going away. Looking up the trail the image would become clearer. In some spots of favorable 'seeing,' we might catch glimpses of a person who had passed days ago, even weeks. Not only might our vision tell us the sex of the person, but also his or her reproductive condition and maybe even something about their position in the social dominance hierarchy (Halfpenny, 2003, p. 16).

Maternal Behaviors:

(Also see *Epimeletic* and *Infantile/Neonatal Behaviors*)

Maternal behaviours are a series of instinctive behaviours including all aspects of whelping, feeding, cleaning and weaning the pups. It also includes actively socializing the pups to their environment, conspecifics and, in the case of dogs, they need to be socialized with the human caretakers involved in their lives.

In wild canids, maternal behaviour continues for almost a year, while pups learn to procure their own food, avoid danger and to participate socially with conspecifics (Sue Alexander, letter to author, July 2007).

Just before labor begins the bitch becomes restless. Once a pup is delivered the mother breaks the sack, and begins to lick the pup. She consumes the waste and begins to nurse. Licking the pup's anus and genitals stimulates the puppies to urinate and defecate, which they cannot, as neonates, do on their own. She eats the feces, and thus keeps the whelping box (nest) clean.

During the first few days after birth the mother leaves the nest only for feeding or elimination. By about five weeks, the mother's milk supply is beginning to decrease and she restricts her nursing to a few short opportunities daily. The domestic dog puppies begin eating moistened puppy food around four-weeks of age. In the wild, the puppies lick the mother's chin and lips to stimulate her to *regurgitate* partially digested food.

Wolf pups beg for food by nudging and licking the mother's mouth, to get her to regurgitate food for them.

Metasignals:

"Metasignals impart information about how other signals should be interpreted. For example, play signals indicate that the subsequent threat signals are not true hostility and should be taken as play" (Lore Haug, letter to author, November 3, 2006).

Metasignals in this ritualized aggressive encounter include: play bow by Airedale, lots of side-to-side movement of the dogs' heads and inhibited biting.

Jaw sparring displays contain many metasignals including: growling and other vocalizations, gaping mouths, ears relatively relaxed, side to side motion of the dogs' heads rather than biting motions aimed with intent to harm.

Play or Threat: How Do Dogs Know Which it Is?

When it is play or ritualized aggression there are many metasignals apparent:

1. Lots of play bowing, even if they are small ones, that are intermingled into other movements.

2. Lots of play "huffing" and other vocalizations.

3. All body language is loose and relaxed.

4. Canids' heads move more laterally (side to side) when a canid "goes in for the kill," rather than a forward and back "stabbing-like" motion that a serious canid intent on causing harm would do.

5. Canids move with a rocking horse gait (see leap run) indicative of play intention.

Mob:

When two or more canids turn *ritualized or agonistic aggressive behavior* toward another.

Barbara Handelman

Three litter mates mob their brother.

Monty Sloan

In this ritualized aggressive attack, several members of the wolf pack mob another of their pack members.

Motivation of Behavior:

Motivation "is what compels an animal to do what it does" (Abrantes, 2005, p. 167).

Hunger motivates hunting, scavenging or begging for food. Sexual urges motivate breeding behaviors, while some sexual behaviors might also result from other types of arousal during play, or from scents in the environment. Fatigue motivates resting or relaxation behaviors. *Fear* might motivate fleeing, *submission*, *freezing*/inaction, or *aggressive behavior*. Threats to an animal's safety, territory or rank within its 'pack' motivate some types of *aggressive behavior*.

Monty Sloan

Fatigue motivates a tired wolf to take a snooze in a hollow log .

Muzzle Grab:

Muzzle grabs are most often soft, inhibited bites that occur during *ritualized aggression* and bouts of play. Occasionally, the biting canid uses enough force to cause pain, in which case the bite would be considered a hard muzzle bite.

Adult canids often muzzle grab young puppies as an attempt to control the pups' behavior. The puppies may first whimper in alarm, but after experiencing a few gentle muzzle grabs they quietly submit without protest.

Monty Sloan

Hard muzzle grab during ritualized aggression. Note agonistic pucker and hard stare from wolf doing the grab. The wolf being grabbed is returning the direct eye contact, but is in a very awkward position; perhaps he is about to roll over into a submissive posture.

Monty Sloan

The wolf on the right is doing a soft muzzle grab. This may be a greeting behavior, or a moment of allogrooming.

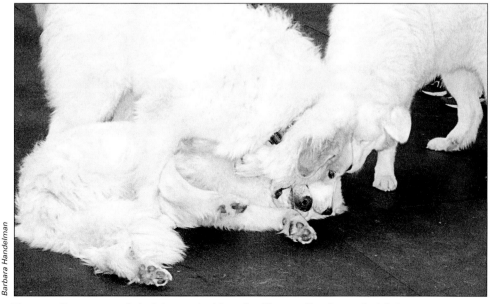

Barbara Handelman

These are littermates at their eight-month-old reunion. The standing dog on the left does a gentle muzzle grab during a bout of play.

167

Dog puppies (left) and wolf puppies (right) do nearly identical muzzle grabs during bouts of play/fighting.

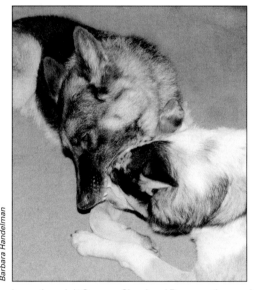

Adult wolves doing a gentle muzzle grab in the same manner as the dog and wolf puppies. In this case, one adult wolf is trying to exert control over another adult.

Luca, the adult German Shepherd Dog, gently muzzle grabs Pan, his young Collie housemate. This is the moment when Luca took control over the interaction following several minutes during which Pan had been allogrooming – washing Luca's face.

Muzzle Nudge:

(Also see *Et-epimeletic*)

Muzzle Punch:

The muzzle punch occurs when a canid uses his muzzle as a weapon in a stabbing motion to the body of another canid or a human. A muzzle punch may be used as a rude greeting, a warning, or as the first blow in a real fight.

Marco De Kloet

Wicked does a muzzle punch during play. Note play bow as metasignal, letting the Bull Dog know this is just play.

Wolf on the right does a paw thwack to the wolf on the left, who looks displeased, but not aroused or agonistic. The paw thwack in this instance is probably an overly enthusiastic pawing behavior, during a moment of obnoxious submission. Note accompanying tongue flick, blink, and ears back that also suggest appeasement or submission.

Photo by Monty Sloan

Section 14:
Neophobia – Pin

Neophobia:

Neophobia: persistent and profound *fear* of new objects in the environment, with poor recovery after exposure. No *fear* of known objects in the environment. Behavior is manifested as severe avoidance, escape behavior or anxiety (Segurson).

Neoteny:

(Also see *Heterochrony,* and *Ontogeny*)

Retention of juvenile characteristics in the adults of a species.

An evolutionary slowing down of bodily development, although sexual development continues. Adults look like the juveniles of their ancestors, although they are capable of sexual reproduction. In truly neotonous or paedomorphic species such as domestic dogs, humans, cattle, sheep, goats and horses, sexual maturity occurs before social maturity (Noakes).

Acquiring a dog may be the only opportunity human ever has to choose a relative.

– Mordecai Siegel

Dogs provide affection without ambivalence, the simplicity of a life free from the almost unbearable conflicts of civilization, the beauty of an existence complete in itself.

– Sigmund Freud

Nibble Groom:

(Also see *Allogrooming*)

Nibble grooming is done exclusively with the front teeth – using rapid, open and shut movement of the jaws. All canids nibble groom themselves, while some will nibble groom other canids, and some even nibble groom human companions (ouch!).

Wolf pup nibble grooms his own foot.

Wolf nibble grooms his packmate's face.

Luca nibble grooms Pan's chest.

Nose Boink:

(Non-scientific term in popular usage. Also see *Muzzle Punch*)

"Nose boinks are usually closed mouthed behaviors. The context for this behavior is as a stress reduction most often occurring at the end of a stressful encounter with a human" (Lore I. Haug, letter to the author, 2007).

Though not exclusive to herding dogs, they are the breeds most apt to display the nose boink behavior. When stressed, any dog might leap at a person's face and 'boink' the person with his muzzle.

The behavior is startling, and the impact may hurt, especially if the 'boink' lands on a human nose. Border Collies and Australian Shepherds from working lines are particularly known for darting in and landing a nose boink on the faces of young children. Adults who hover over a dog with their faces too close to the dog's face may also get boinked.

The nose boink behavior does not have agonistic intent. It may occur in any setting when the dog has been stressed by an intense interaction with a human. In the case of Herding breeds, it may be related to herding behavior. It is not unusual for a herding dog to dart in and 'boink' a sheep that won't turn with the flock, perhaps adding a nip for emphasis. (Such a nip when landed on the thick skin of a sheep or cow would do no harm.)

Paedomorphosis:

(Also see *Domestication, Heterochrony, Neoteny, Play*)

"The retention of juvenile morphology at maturity, is thought to be an important process in generating evolutionary novelties" (Goodwin et al., 1996 p. 297).

Parallel Walking:

(Also see *Allelomimetic Behavior)*

Parallel walking refers to instances when two canids move companionably side by side, matching the length of their strides to each other's. This may occur during *courtship* but is not exclusive to that activity. Brenda Aloff calls this type of behavior "mirroring" (Aloff, 2005, p. 207).

Parallel movement might be a more appropriate term, since canids' synchronized matching of stride length is not limited to the walking gait.

Two dogs of very different sizes walk companionably together, matching the length of their strides in order to remain side by side with each other.

Two white wolves walking in perfectly matched step with each other.

Two dogs of different size match each other stride for stride at a canter.

Parallel movement may also occur when:

- Pups are learning to hunt
- Sled dogs are freed from traces of a sled
- During pre-predatory behavior (just before a hunt begins)
- Just before *predatory drift* during play.

Pawing:

(Also see *Et-Epimeletic Behavior*)

Pawing is usually gentle, and used to initiate a playful interaction. It is also a form of *redirected behavior,* which dog pups use with adult dogs and humans. It harks back to life in the wild where wolf and other canid puppies lick and paw at the adult dogs to elicit the adult canid to *regurgitate* food.

Puppy pawing directed toward the human, eliciting attention.

Sibling interaction, dog on the right pawing the head of the dog on left – play invitation.

Pup on right gently pawing his friend, trying to elicit his attention, and perhaps inviting him to play.

Wolf pups attempt to elicit regurgitation of food, using pawing and muzzle nudging.

Paw-lift:

Paw-lifts can indicate uncertainty, or may be a metasignal warning that agonistic behavior is coming next. Also the paw-lift can occur as a part of the "point" which is a fixed action pattern in certain breeds.

Pan does an exaggerated paw-lift, while approaching Luca who has a bone. The downward tilt of Pan's head and his ears at half-mast suggest appeasement. His whiskers are flared forward, indicating some degree of arousal at the same time.

Dog above is stressed. He is doing a submissive paw-lift, while tucking his tail and doing a submissive grin.

Pan's paw-lift is a sign of his peaceful intentions and calm greeting.

Border Collie's paw-lift is a warning to the other dog of increasing tension and decreasing tolerance for the Collie's intrusive behaviors. Both dogs are very stiff, legs straight, heads held high.

These Great Pyrenees puppies are jaw wrestling. The pup on the left does an exaggerated paw-lift as a metasignal that says "this is just play".

Border Collie does an exaggerated paw-lift during a meeting with another male. The two dogs circled each other, doing a bit of growling, accompanied by wagging tails. The exaggerated paw-lift may have been a metasignal, a warning that aggression was about to begin – and likely would have, had humans not intervened.

Monty Sloan

Paw-lift and tongue flicks are gestures of appeasement.

Monty Sloan

Wolf in the middle is displaying active submission – he has lowered his body to a crouch. He is doing an exaggerated paw-lift, and head turn.

Paw Over Back:

Placing a paw over another canid's back is a *dominance* action, or an action intended to convey which animal controls the situation. The paw over the back may also be a prelude to a *ride up*.

Barbara Handelman

Louie places a paw over Pan's back; this is likely an invitation to play, but Pan looks uncertain.

Sabarika

Husky places a paw over the back of the black dog as a prelude to a ride up.

Paw Thwack:

Overly exuberant use of the paw and foreleg to strike another canid on top of the head. May be part of play or *ritualized aggression.* Or it may spark true *aggression,* if the animal who gets "thwacked" doesn't appreciate the force of the action, or the intent of the action is to provoke a reaction.

Two Irish Wolfhounds engaged in rough play. Dog on left lands a paw thwack to the head of his playmate.

Wolf on right does a paw thwack to wolf lying down.

Penis Crowning:

Penis crowning is very different from an erection. Penis crowning is a physiological response to excitement and various forms of arousal including sexual and agonistic aggression. According to Dr. Lore Haug (letter to the author, March 28, 2007), "penis crowning is just a protrusion of the penis from the prepuce; an erection is actual vascular engorgement of the penis, both of these can occur independently of the other.

Luca, the retired German Shepherd, gets aroused each time Pan is about to go out to work for their disabled handler – a job that used to belong to Luca. In this instance, the mounting and penis crowning are part of a dominance display.

This is a fairly intense play interaction between two males. The dog on the right exhibits penis crowning.

Pica:

(Also see *Polydipsea, Coprophagia*)

The persistent consumption of non-food substances such as dirt, rocks, feces, paper, etc.

177

Piloerector Reflex (Raised Hackles):

Most often, canids display their raised hackles when they are surprised, fearful or aroused. While piloerection may communicate aggressive arousal or *agonistic* intent, it is a misconception that canids' raised hackles primarily indicate *aggressive behavior*.

The human equivalent of a canid's raised hackles takes the form of "goose bumps". Goose bumps commonly occur at times of extreme stress or *fear* (or when the person is cold).

Piloerection takes various forms that are not solely dependent on coat length. Some dogs' hackles rise only on their shoulders; some display hackles from the tops of their head down the length of their tails; and others look comical when their hackles rise only at the ruff of the neck and on their rumps. Some canids take on the appearance of a "blow fish," as their hackles rise not only over the entire length of their backs, but also along their sides.

Sabarika

Note: piloerector reflex in the smooth coated dog on the left.

Barbara Handelman

Tucker, the Australian Shepherd, displays a piloerector reflex that makes him look like a blowfish, while he stands over Pan the Collie.

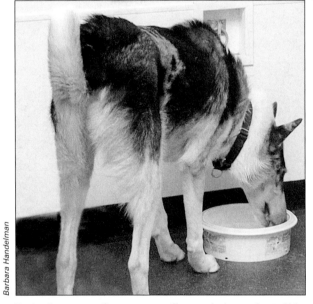

Barbara Handelman

Pan's piloerector reflex response effects only the portions of his coat over his shoulders and rump.

Monty Sloan

This wolf's piloerector reflex runs down the entire length of his back.

Pin:

Pinning the body of an opponent occurs when one animal uses the weight of his body or grabs the throat or muzzle of another – most often with an inhibited bite – forcing the other animal to the ground. Pinning may occur during play, *ritualized aggression* or during a serious attack with intent to do harm.

A wolf pup and a young Great Dane pup are play wrestling. The wolf pup has pinned the Dane.

This is a ritualized aggressive interaction. The wolf on top is pinning the wolf on bottom, who has offered passive submissive posture – signifying his defeat in this encounter. The wolf on the right is the alpha male, ready to intervene if the other two boys get carried away.

The Pit Bull pinned the Airedale during a vigorous play session. The pin is incomplete, self-interrupted by the Pit Bull, who did not follow through with a neck bite or other injurious act. This photo illustrates that a well-socialized Pit Bull can play appropriately with other dogs. These three dogs had frequent opportunities to play together and are known to enjoy each other's play styles. They are always supervised, so that no dog has the opportunity to become overly aroused. Humans choose the moment to end the play session on a positive note.

Composite time-lapse photo. Dog with very loose flews displays play face and rocking horse gait while engaged in locomotory play.

Photo by Marco De Kloet

Section 15:
Play – Play Face

(Also see *Metasignals, Ritualized Aggression, Socialization*)

Categories of Play:
Locomotory Play, Object Play, Predatory Play, and Social Play (Includes Play Fighting)

> Play is all motor activity performed postnatally that *appears* (italics theirs) to be purposeless, in which motor patterns from other contexts may often be used in modified forms and altered temporal sequencing. If the activity is directed towards another living being, it is called *play* (italics theirs) (Bekoff and Byers, 1981, p. 300-1).

Metasignals that occur during canine interactions help to define those behaviors that are, in fact, play. *Metasignals* are extremely important. Some postures used during play also appear in threat/warnings that signal the onset of fights. Both the canid participants and human observers can depend on *metasignals* to reveal the true motivation and likely outcome of canine interactions.

Seven-week-old puppies playing. Pinned puppy offers agonistic pucker to express her displeasure, and uses her paws to push her sister off.

Locomotory Play

Barbara Handelman

Pan and Louie engage in locomotory play, both using a rocking horse style gait as they run together.

Object Play:

Most canids, both puppies and adults, engage in object play. Object play is often a form of *investigatory behavior*. The objects may be toys provided by humans, or sticks, leaves, tree branches, pieces of hide, or any other object of interest in the environment. Canids engage in both solo object play and interactive object play.

Interactive Object Play:

Barbara Handelman

Luca engaged in an intense game of tug with the author's husband.

Monty Sloan

Wolf pups playing tug with littermates for opponents.

- Chasing a ball or other object thrown by a human.

Barbara Handelman

Barbara Handelman

Pan plays fetch with gusto, for about 6 or 8 retrieves – then he is done. He actually has limited interest in chasing balls or other toys, which correlates with his non-predatory attitude towards rodents and cats. He has curiosity about small critters, but is disinclined to chase them. He approaches rodents much the same way he does cats, by moving toward them very slowly in an arc rather than straight on. He appears much happier when his quarry remains still so he can watch and perhaps befriend them, and seems disappointed if they run. He does not chase them.

Luca is very intense about retrieving. His strong ball drive is related to intense predatory drive. Luca chases rodents and cats with the same intensity as he retrieves toys. For Luca, retrieving is part of an incomplete predatory sequence (see fixed action patterns). His is playing with his favorite toy: a Go-Far® ball with a slingshot-like rubber band attached.

Monty Sloan

This socialized wolf was actually retrieving sticks thrown for him by humans.

Solo Object Play:
- Chewing toys or found objects relieves pain caused by erupting adult teeth

Monty Sloan

Two wolf pups chew on the same stick.

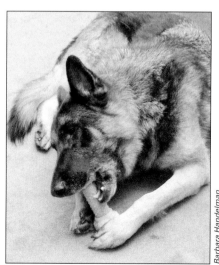

Barbara Handelman

Chewing toys and found objects relieves stress and boredom.

- Chasing, throwing and catching leaves, balls, or other toys. Recreational/ relaxation behavior that is pleasurable and relieves boredom.

A wolf entertains himself with a Frisbee®.

- Solo tugging, manipulating, or chewing on found objects or toys.

Pan engages in a solo game of tug with a rope attached to a door.

Playing with interactive toy that dispenses treat.

Searching for treats hidden by a human.

Predatory Play:

(Also see *Predation Sequence* and *Fixed Action Patterns*)

A complex set of behaviors used to rehearse hunting skills.

Predatory play behaviors include:

- Alerting or orienting with an intent stare in dog-to-dog interaction.

This dog is orienting and targeting another dog who has just come into view.

- Stalking

Louie is stalking Pan in this predatory play interaction.

- Chasing: where the "predator" chases only fast enough to keep up – not fast enough to actually catch the "prey". Often roles will reverse in the middle of the game.

Predatory play chase.

Three dogs participate in predatory play: note play face expressions on first two dogs.

- Inhibited biting at front leg

Barbara Handelman

Airedale is doing an inhibited, predatory front leg bite which could be used to disable a prey animal or a canine opponent.

- Inhibited hock bite

Monty Sloan

The wolf in the rear is going for a hind leg, a bite that could cripple prey or disable a canine opponent.

- Inhibited neck bite

Marco De Kloet

Inhibited bite to the neck of dog in the role of "prey".

Marco De Kloet

Inhibited bite to the neck of dog in the role of "prey".

•   Inhibited neck bites continued

Marco De Kloet

Dog in the center is the "prey". One dog comes over the top with a bite to the neck, while another aims straight for his neck. Notice that the "prey" dog is relaxed. His lips are long, his eyes squinty, and his body is loose. This is play.

Marco De Kloet

Wicked has taken the Pointer down for the pin and the kill bite in this predatory play interaction. Notice how relaxed the Pointer is, his tail is level with his body and wagging, his lips are long, and his body loose – he is unconcerned and fully into the "game".

•   Pin

Monty Sloan

The pin in this instance is a component of social play/ritualized aggression. The pin serves to define the canid on top as the victor after the canid below submits. This could be a contest of strength and confidence. The canid who submits chooses his position rather than risk injury. Roles may reverse in subsequent mock battles. If this is a hierarchy contest among low ranking wolf pack members, the outcome is usually predetermined as pack status is generally stable. Low ranking wolves may engage each other in ritualized aggression in an effort to move up the hierarchical ladder, but contests for the position of alpha occur very rarely.

Kill Shake:

The kill shake, although part of the *predation, fixed action pattern*, is occurring out of contextual order and thus can easily be identified as part of *object play*, with predatory characteristics.

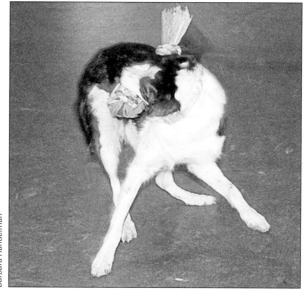

Border Collie is doing kill shake behavior during object play with a rope toy.

Kill Toss:

Like the *kill shake*, the kill toss appears in the course of *object play*, and can be distinguished as play by the fact that it is happening outside the context and set order of the *predation fixed action pattern*.

A ten-week-old Pit Bull puppy does a mouse jump, biting then shaking and tossing a mechanical mouse. Most adult dogs are wary of this toy mouse because of the noises it emits and the taste of its mechanical parts. This puppy had unusually intense predatory behavior. She would not be a safe pet in a home with young children who moved quickly.

Killing Bite During Play:

(Also see *Predation Fixed Action Pattern*)

Killing bites may vary in type. Whatever the type, it occurs in the same place in the *predation* sequence (after bite, and before dissect). In an actual fight (the killing bite comes toward the end of the predatory sequence), a dog might be bitten many times before the kill bite occurs. Some dogs bite the throat of another dog, latch on and actually suffocate their opponent by constricting its windpipe. Another type of kill bite occurs when one dog grabs another dog's throat and then proceeds to shake the dog, potentially breaking its neck.

During *ritualized aggression* the observer might see lots of grab and shake behavior, even in young puppies. The kill bite behavior happening out of order in the *predation sequence,* or happening in the absence of other components of the sequence, is one way to differentiate *ritualized aggressive behavior* from *aggressive behavior* with intent to do harm.

Barbara Handelman

Kill bite in the context of play.

Barbara Handelman

Luca has Pan by the throat in a grip that could kill the puppy.
Good thing they both know that this is ritualized aggression –
not the real thing.

Social Play:

Most *social play* includes some elements of the predatory sequence in which canids adopt and swap the roles of prey and predator. From as early as the second or third week in the whelping box, dogs can be seen practicing jaw wrestling, and other "mock fighting" (*ritualized aggressive behavior*). Usually, *social play* is practice for "fight or flight" in real-life situations.

Play is the context in which puppies learn to communicate. They learn from both their mother's and their littermates' reactions, how their own behavior prompts or changes the behavior of other canids (*conspecifics*).

As they mature, puppies need to socialize with other canids so they can further develop their communication skills. It is in the context of play that they refine their abilities to communicate. Opportunities for *social play* with *conspecifics* are essential throughout the pups' development – into adolescence and young adulthood. As they mature, pups that grow up in relative isolation often become either fearful of, or aggressive toward, other canids, despite having been born with otherwise stable temperaments.

All pups should be introduced to children and adults while still with their litters. Once in their forever homes, they should attend puppy kindergarten classes, starting around ten to twelve-weeks-of-age. The classes should allow ample, well-supervised time for pups to socialize with other healthy puppies.

There is evidence that poor – or non-existent – early *socialization*, is a major contributor to young dogs being abandoned, or sentenced to death by euthanasia in shelters. Pups can be carefully socialized with other pups by having private puppy parties with healthy, partially immunized pups, in an environment that has not previously been utilized by dogs with unknown health histories. Dog parks should be avoided until the pups are fully immunized and comfortable with other dogs of all ages and sizes.

According to Robert K. Anderson, DVM, at the University of Minnesota College of Veterinary Medicine,

> ....the risk of a dog dying (euthanasia) because of behavior problems is 1,000 times the risk of dying of distemper or parvo virus. Early learning, socialization of puppies, and appropriate vaccination should go together in a wellness program designed to protect lives of dogs and improve the bond with families.

> Social play is an excellent example of a behavior that both feels good and is important for survival. The shared joy experienced during play connects individuals and regulates interactions. Play is easy to discern from other behaviors. Individuals become deeply immersed in the activity and show their delight by their acrobatic movements, gleeful vocalizations, and smiles. They play hard, get exhausted, rest, and go at it again and again.

> Studies of the chemistry of play support the idea that play is fun. Neuroscientist, Steve Siviy, has shown that dopamine (and perhaps serotonin and norephinephrine) is important in the regulation of play, and that large regions of the brain are active during play. Rats show an increase in dopamine activity, simply anticipating the opportunity to play.

> These findings suggest that there are neurochemical bases for why play is enjoyable, and that the same chemical changes occur in both animals and humans during play. In other words, a boy and his dog wrestling in the yard are not only both playing – they both understand that they are playing, and they're getting the same pleasurable feelings from doing so (Bekoff, 2007, p 55-56).

During *social play*, the observer will note play postures and facial expressions including, but not limited to:

- *Bowing*
- *Boxing*
- *Chasing*
- *Clasping*
- *Feinting*
- *Foreleg Stabs*
- *Freezes*

- *Hiding, "surprise attacks"*
- *Inhibited Biting*
- *Jaw Wrestling*
- **Leaping**
- *Parrying*
- *Pawing*
- *Pinning*

- *Play Faces*
- *Pouncing*
- *Rocking horse style gait*
- *Role Reversals*
- *Squashing*
- *Self-Handicapping* during which the players do not play any harder than the weakest player can tolerate

A *bow* is one form of *metasignal*. Play *bow*s also serve to maintain a "play mood" when interspersed among other behaviors that might be misinterpreted as *agonistic*.

Sabarika

Great Dane puppy invites other dogs to chase him.

Sabarika

Bow as an invitation to play.

Monty Sloan

Bow as an invitation to play or chase.

Sabarika

Curving body lines and exaggerated movements signal the dog's desire to play.

Monty Sloan

Wolf on the left issues a "play chase" invitation, to which the other wolf responds by starting to chase after him.

- Puppies learn to modulate the intensity of the physical force employed when biting playmates during *social play* interactions. If they bite too hard, their playmate complains vocally and may withdraw – thus ending the desired play interaction.

Monty Sloan

Wolf pup on the left has a mouth full of skin and is pulling hard. The other pup does not look happy about it.

- If a pup playfully bites an adult canid using too much force, the pup may be "reprimanded" vocally, given a hard stare, or have a paw placed on his body that unequivocally stops the pup's activity. The adult eloquently conveys that the pup crossed over the boundary line of appropriate play behavior.

- During *social play* interactions, roles reverse frequently (the pursuer becomes the pursued), allowing *conspecifics* to practice dominant and submissive interaction patterns.

Play Fighting:

(Also see *Ritualized Aggression* and *Metasignals*)

Play fighting is actually a subset of *social play*. Play fighting is rehearsal for true combative interactions with *conspecifics*: e.g. resolving territorial disputes; ostracizing errant, weak, or victimized pack members (wolves and other wild canids); settling hierarchical disputes (relevant to wolves and other wild canids, not domestic dogs); other "fight or flight" survival behaviors. Play fighting also serves as a way *conspecifics* can test the relative health and strength of another canid, before entering into any serious contest over control of resources.

Play sometimes evolves into *ritualized aggression* and from there may tip over into a real fight, if *metasignals* (indicating play intention) are either ignored or misperceived. *Ritualized aggressive* contests, conserve strength and reduce risk of injury – which in the wild could lead to death from blood loss, infection, or starvation due to inability to hunt.

Play fighting behaviors include:

- Chasing

Two wolves are chasing each other playfully. This interaction may be part of play fighting, while also being an example of locomotory play.

- Leg biting (hamstringing opponent)

Pan bites Daisy's back leg as he might to an opponent in a real fight, or to a prey animal smaller than he is.

- Inhibited biting of the neck or other body parts that would disable an opponent

Monty Sloan

The wolf on the right is about to land an inhibited bite on the hind quarters of his playmate. A serious bite in this location could cripple a prey animal or an opponant in a fight.

- Take Down

Kevin Peuhkurinen

A bite to the spinal cord in the region of the neck would easily disable an opponent in an actual attack. In this instance, the aggression is ritualized in the context of a play interaction. Note the rocking horse style/leap run gait which makes it clear that this is play. If this were a bite to a prey animal or opponent, the biting canid would hold on as he proceded to take the other animal down.

- Standing or walking tall (confident posture)

Monty Sloan

This wolf's confidence is evident in his upright posture, tail raised – level with his back – and ears forward.

See sections for the following *ritualized aggressive behaviors: Feinting and Parrying; Boxing; Foreleg Stabs; Paw Thwacks;* inhibited choke hold bite to the neck, with or without head shaking.

- Standing Over

The standing wolf maintains a confident posture, he is clearly in command of the situation. The wolf below has conceded victory to the standing wolf... his posture portrays submission. He displays passive submission by lying on his side, tail tucked, ears back, eyes averted, and doing a tongue flick.

- Squash: after *pinning* or taking down an opponent, the vanquishing canid might sit or lie upon the defeated canid.

The wolf on top is squashing the wolf beneath him.

Play Face:

"Lips horizontally retracted, jaws slightly open, ears pulled straight up and back, or simply folded flat back." (Goodman, et al., 2002, p. 23)

Sabarika

Two dogs face each other, each with a "play face" expression – long lips, mouths open, ears tilted back, Their tails are also held high over their backs, and their stiff front legs suggest their next moves will initiate a play interaction, such as a pounce or play chase.

Monty Sloan

Wolf displaying play face as he approaches familiar humans. Note: his lips are long, and his mouth is open in a non-threatening display of affiliative intension.

Marco De Kloet

Wicked with play face expression, long lips, mouth open as he appears to fly over the sand, no feet touching the ground.

197

An 8-week-old Great Pyranees puppy
plays with a favorite stuffed toy.

Photo by Barbara Handelman

Section 16:
Play in Domestic Dogs – Puppy License

Evolutionary changes and selective breeding –
the impact on play in domestic dogs:

Selective breeding has changed the morphology of dogs (physical structure), bringing about *paedomorphosis*: the retention of juvenile morphology at maturity (Goodwin, et al., 1996, p. 297). Domestic dogs engage in *social play* over the span of their lifetimes, but are most playful as puppies and during adolescence. Most *social play* among wolves occurs during infancy and *courtship*.

Selective breeding of domestic dogs has altered some of the facial structures involved in adult *agonistic* displays. Adult dogs generally display fewer submissive behaviors than their wolf and coyote cousins.

Wolves use *agonistic* displays to warn and diffuse rising antagonism, and to prevent encounters from escalating to serious fights. Human intervention both during and after *Agonistic* encounters between dogs, lessens the necessity for dogs to use submissive behaviors to de-escalate arousal levels. Dogs therefore have lost depth and range from both ends of the continuum of their repertoire of *aggression* communication and *submission* displays.

Play-like behavior in adult wolves occurs in the course of pack hierarchy contests. Most testing of strength and confidence occur in the context of *ritualized aggression*. Except in rare all-out battles, most conflicts between wolves are resolved through bouts of *ritualized aggression* in which one wolf emerges from the encounter as the dominant victor, and the other wolf chooses to submit rather than risk injury.

Actual challenges for the position of *alpha* among wolves are rare. Underlings move up and down the pack hierarchy ladder over the course of their lives in the pack. "Dogs may have an entirely different social organization, in fact they are likely not pack animals" (Sue Alexander, Letter to Author, August 2007).

The rules of "Game Theory and Evolutionary Stable Strategies" (Prestwich) apply when discussing the differences between play and attacks:

> In general, actual aggression only occurs if the aggressor is certain of a win. Otherwise, too much energy is expended in attempting to engage the opponent and the result will be expended energy in the fight as well as the energy required to heal from any resulting injury (Sue Alexander, Letter to Author, August 2007).

Paedomorphosis is particularly relevant as it applies to the facial structures that are active in signaling *agonistic* and *submissive behaviors*. Research suggests (see Goodwin, et al., 1996) that *paedomorphosis* has also altered the frequency and intensity of both *agonistic* and *submissive* behavioral displays in domestic dogs. Some breeds have retained more wolf-like morphological characteristics than others, thus retaining more of the wolf's signaling behaviors. Markings, especially those that highlight the eyes, accentuate and thus make facial expressions more readily "readable" (see *facial markings*).

According to Goodwin et al., attempts to genetically reintroduce more wolflike signaling behaviors have failed.

"The function of these signals within the wolf pack is largely to prevent the escalation of aggression...." (Goodwin, et al., 1997, p. 302-303)

Opportunities to play and interact with other canids are essential to the healthy development of all puppies. Without such opportunities, puppies become fearful, aggressive, or both fearful and aggressive – largely because of their inability to accurately "read" the communication displays of *conspecifics*. Puppies isolated from other puppies and adult dogs also fail to learn the range of skills they will need to negotiate encounters with *conspecifics* that will occur during their lifetimes.

Play Styles:

Play styles vary among domestic dog breeds and mixes of breeds. For example, herding breeds (Border Collies, Aussies, German Shepherd Dogs, Corgis, etc.) tend to circle, "head" (interrupt movement by moving in front), and bite at the heels of their playmates. "Bully breeds" (American Pit Bull Terriers, Staffordshire Terriers, Boxers, etc.) are apt to be more physical, engage in more *body slamming, wrestling* and intense *jaw sparring*.

> Breed-Related play styles of domestic dogs follow the fixed action pattern modifications related to breed-specific jobs such as: hunting with humans, guarding livestock for humans, tracking and other search behaviors, as well as police and other protection training.

Polydipsea:

(Also see *Stereotypic Behaviors*)

Chronic excessive drinking.

The behavior may occur independent of thirst. Polydipsea may be symptomatic of a health issue such as diabetes. Some canids drink excessively in response to stress. Chronic excessive drinking in the absence of a medical condition may be a form of *stereotypic behavior*.

Polyphagia:

(Also see *Pica*)

Chronic excessive eating.

Domestic dogs are opportunistic and some will eat to excess if they gain access to a store of food. Canids in the wild will eat until they are satiated whenever they make a kill, or scavenge carrion. They might not have the need or opportunity to eat again for several days. Occasional consumption of a large amount of food does not constitute polyphagia. Canids who chronically consume both food and non-food substances may have both polyphagia and *pica*.

Pounce:

(Also see *Locomotory Play, Predatory Play, Predation*)

A pounce is a movement used both in predatory behavior and play. Canids pounce to kill small prey, like mice, voles, and other rodents.

> To jump on a life form or something exhibiting some qualities of a life form, such as out-of -sight rustling in tall grass. The "pouncee" is often pinned with the jaws. Historically called the "mouse jump" or "mouse pounce" (Goodman, et al., 2002, p. 24).

Wicked in mid-air playfully pouncing on the dog below – who appears to be rolling in the sand, oblivious to Wicked's impending descent. Then again, he may be rolling over in order to submit... too late to deter Wicked's landing on him.

Wicked pounces during play with the Dachshund. He is poised to land near him, but not on him.

Man is troubled by what might be called the Dog Wish, a strange and involved compulsion to be as happy and carefree as a dog.

– James Thurber, in Thurber's Dogs

Lure coursing Whippet catches his prey.

Photo by Diane Lewis

Section 17: Predation

Predatory Motor Patterns

Predation is the act of obtaining food by killing and consuming prey. Canids are able to vary the motor patterns, and may engage in one stage of the motor pattern without following a specific sequence. The predatory motor pattern includes most – sometimes all – of the following behaviors:

- Scan and scent
- Orient
- Freeze
- Stalk
- Charge, pounce (Also called foreleg-stab or mouse jump) or chase
- Grab bite
- Kill bite
- Toss
- Dissect
- Consume or cache

Most domestic dogs do not have to hunt in order to eat. Through selective breeding their hunting related motor patterns have been altered so that they can successfully fulfill niche careers in service of humans. Some phases of the predatory motor patterns have been hypertrophied (strengthened), while others have been greatly diminished.

Some species of predator can substitute one motor pattern for another. Wolves, coyotes, and foxes can substitute a forefoot-stab called a "mouse jump" for the chase motor pattern:

orient > eye-stalk > forefoot-stab > kill-bite > dissect > consume

...The canids have several kill-bites. One common variation is the head-shake:

orient > eye-stalk > chase > grab-bite > head shake > dissect > consume

...In some species, one motor pattern is wired together with the next one in the sequence. The first motor pattern releases the second, while the second releases the third, and so on. Some animals cannot perform the grab-bite unless they have chased, and cannot chase unless they have stalked, and so on back up the line.

...Unlike the cat family, the dog family tends not to have the predatory motor patterns tightly wired together. Canids can begin the predatory sequence starting with any motor pattern, which is why they make such great scavengers (Coppinger, 2001, p. 206-208).

Dogs have been bred selectively for hundreds of years to accommodate the needs of their human partners. By selecting for one or more features of the *predation sequence*, herding dogs diverged from natural predators, to dogs who control or protect livestock without harming or overstressing their flocks.

In the Border Collie, the *eye-stalk* and chase motors patterns are hypertrophied, while the *kill-bite, dissect* and *consume motors patterns* are diminished. Border Collies will bite a sheep – sometimes on cue – if a recalcitrant sheep refuses to change course. Border Collies may also bite at their own initiative if a sheep charges them, or when the dog has become frustrated or overly aroused while herding. It is rare to see a Border Collie draw blood, and rarer still to see one injure or kill a sheep.

iStockphoto.com/Kate Leigh

A Border Collie grips a sheep that has split from the flock. Gripping – biting, or biting and holding on – is considered a fault in herding trials. Gripping may be a necessity when the dog is actually working the flock, and some dogs will do it on cue.

Hunting dogs have also been selectively bred for their hypertrophied *eye-stalk* and carry (retrieve) while their *chase, kill bite, dissect* and *consume motor patterns* are greatly diminished.

Wolves are primarily cursory hunters. When they approach a herd, they single out either a young, old, or weakened animal to chase. The wolves run the prey animal until it is near exhaustion, only then do they attack. When hunting large prey animals such as moose or bison, wolves hunt cooperatively with other wolves and work together to bring the animal down by grabbing hold of the neck, spine, flank and nose of their prey. One wolf might grip the nose, while another grabs and holds onto the underside of the animal's neck, in an effort to suffocate it. Another might grab high on the animal's rear flank to disable a leg. Wolves rarely attack a large animal at bay, because they risk injury to themselves from front and rear leg strikes and goring by antlers or horns.

It is commonly thought that the wolf's usual method of killing is by hamstringing, or cutting the large Achilles' tendon....

...It is tempting to give some measure of belief to such reports when they are made by so many observers. However, these "records" are directly contradicted by the results of every modern study of the wolf's killing tactics. Either wolves have changed their ways, or the old reports were in error.

It does seem possible that when wolves depended a great deal on livestock for prey, hamstringing might have been useful to disable an individual. Domestic animals have been protected by man for so long that they are not so quick and agile as wild species. Perhaps wolves could close in on them and slash their hamstrings without getting kicked by their hind hooves (Mech, 1970, p. 204).

This photo makes very clear why attempting to hamstring large prey animals could prove extremely dangerous for the predator.

According to Coppinger (2001, p. 207), "the weak-jawed dog family tears flesh, bleeding the prey to death". The method by which canids kill their prey depends not only on the strength of the canid but also on the size of the prey. Prey animals larger than the canid are most likely to be killed by canids hunting cooperatively and using some combination of crushing the trachea, severing the spinal cord, and blood loss due to torn flesh. Small prey animals such as rodents or birds are most likely to be killed by a combination of crushing, shaking and tossing.

Dogs that hunt and retrieve birds have been selectively bred over the centuries for their hypertrophied *eye-stalk* and carry (retrieve), while their *chase, kill bite, dissect* and *consume motor patterns* are greatly reduced.

Scan:

Kevin Peuhkurinen

Two Irish Wolfhounds visually scan the field looking for deer.

www.atourhands.com/coursing.html

A Whippet orients after spotting its prey.

Orient:

Monty Sloan

A wolf orients and stares (gives eye) in the direction of his prey.

Freeze:

istockphoto.com/Lawrence Sawyer

An English Pointer freezes on point after spotting a bird.

Monty Sloan

A wolf freezes while stalking his prey.

Eye Stalking:

iStockphoto.com/Joop Shijder

A Border Collie uses his intense eye-stalking (gives eye) to convince the sheep in his care to turn and rejoin the flock. Notice how the eye-stalking of the Border Collie is similar to that of the wolf below. His mouth is open because he is panting.

Monty Sloan

A wolf gives eye (uses eye-stalking) to "test" his prey, challenging the bison to turn and run. A wolf will not charge large prey animals that are "at bay" – standing their ground prepared to fight. The risk to the wolf's own safety is too great.

istockphoto.com/Robert Churchill

Two Border Collies work a flock of sheep cooperatively, each receiving his own directions from the shepherd. They have successfully gathered the sheep together. Depending on the shepherd's signals, they will next pressure the sheep to move in a specified direction. They work at a distance from the sheep. If they get closer, they will create too much pressure and the sheep may panic. There is always a "lead sheep" whom the dogs identify and watch. When the leader turns her head the flock will follow her in the direction in which her head turned. The dogs are prepared to either cut off the flock's escape, or encourage its movement, as the shepherd directs them. The Border Collies' predatory action patterns appear very similar to those of the wolves, below, but are not intended to earn themselves a meal.

Testing:

When hunting large prey animals, canids work cooperatively to test the herd and to select out the young, the old, and the injured as their chosen target for the hunt. The canids will dart in close, *bow*, and move away quickly to keep themselves out of harm's way. Both the wolves and the bison are sizing each other up, testing each other's strength and stamina. The *bow* is often the posture of choice when testing. From the *bow* position, a canid can move easily and quickly in any direction.

Monty Sloan

Monty Sloan

The wolves in thesse photos move in, bow, and retreat to test the fitness of a potential prey animal.

Wearing and Lateral Movements:

iStockphoto.com/Kate Leigh

The Border Collie is "wearing" – moving laterally from side to side behind the sheep either to "fetch" the sheep and move them toward the shepherd or to "drive" them away toward a pen or another field. By "wearing," the dog keeps the sheep moving in a relatively straight line, not allowing them to drift off course in either direction.

Monty Sloan

The wolf moves laterally in order to turn the calf and his mother, perhaps looking for an opportunity to separate the two, or move them in the direction of other pack members with whom he is hunting cooperatively. The wolf's lateral movements bear striking similarity to the movements of the Border Collie while wearing and fetching his flock of sheep.

Chase:

Kevin Peuhkurinen

Three Sight Hounds chase after a lure. Despite the great difference in their stride length, they appear to be matching each other stride for stride, in alleleomimetic parallel movement.

Kevin Peuhkurinen

An Afgan Hound chases his prey.

Charge or Pounce:

A wolf does a mouse jump as a substitute for the chase phase in the predatory motor pattern.

A wolf does a mouse pounce out on the ice. It is hard to know what he sees with his intent expression. It is likely something is moving on or under the ice.

Coyote puppy does a *mouse jump.*

Grab Bite:

In some parts of the world, lure coursing is still an inhumane blood sport – culminating with the grab, crushing kill-bite and dissection of the live rabbit lure.

This Borzoi is lure coursing in North America, where the sport is humane for the dogs and the inanimate lure.

213

A Greyhound grabs the lure in a dramatic kill bite.

Kill Bite:

After the kill bite, the dog goes over the top of the lure as he might a live animal whose spine would surely be broken in the process.

Cache or Consume:

iStockphoto.com/Waldemar Dabrowski

A Labrador Retriever carries a duck back to the hunter who shot it. He uses such a soft mouth that he will not leave a mark on the bird. The dissect and consume phases of his predatory motor patterns have diminished, while this dog retains the retrieve phase which resembles the carry phase demonstrated by the fox and coyote.

Monty Sloan

A fox carries the mouse that he has killed off to a safe place where he can eat undisturbed, or he might deliver it to his mate and their kits, or cache the meal for later consumption.

iStockphoto.com/Michael Thompson

A coyote carries a recently killed Canada Goose. He may be intending to feast on it himself or to deliver it to his mate and puppies for a shared meal. Or, he might cache it for later consumption.

Monty Sloan

A wolf dining on a rack of ribs.

Wolf pups nudge the throat of an adult wolf
hoping for a regurgitated meal.
Photo by Monty Sloan

Section 18:
Puppy Behavior – Regurgitate

Puppy Behavior/Socialization

The primary socialization period of puppies is between 3 and 13 weeks. This period is critical for development of primary social relationships with humans and other animals. Puppies that are confined during this period are significantly more likely to develop behavioral problems (primarily *fear* and *aggression*) than puppies that are provided a socialization program. Puppies isolated from *conspecifics* (other puppies) until 16 weeks of age, were significantly more likely to display fearful behavior and be aggressed upon by other pups. They were unable to develop a positive relationship with other dogs. Puppies raised in isolation until 16 weeks lose the capacity to exhibit playful behavior toward strangers. Previous research demonstrates that socialization is a critical step in the development of behaviorally healthy dogs.

Puppies with parvovirus die within a few weeks of contacting the virus; puppies with behavior problems die within a few years. Because of the temporal disconnect between acquiring the disease (behavior or parvovirus) and mortality, the need to develop comprehensive socialization programs in puppies is often underestimated. Dogs surrendered to a shelter are most likely to have been initially acquired from a shelter. This data does not reveal whether the relinquishers valued the dog less because they obtained it from a shelter, whether they returned it because of behavior problems which started before they obtained the dog (in the shelter or before entry to the shelter), or some other factor. A recent study demonstrated that puppies who attended socialization classes were more likely to be retained in their homes than those that did not.

Behavioral problems are the primary cause of relinquishment of dogs to shelters. Thus, they are also the leading primary cause of mortality of dogs in animal shelters. Because the signs of behavior problems are not as blatant as parvovirus, behavior problem prevention in puppies is not a primary focus of many animal shelters. Shelters can and should develop socialization programs for puppies which maximize socialization AND protect them from infectious diseases (Segurson, 2007, p. 3-4).

Puppy License:

Dogs also have a timetable in their heads – puppies under 16 weeks of age can usually take appalling liberties with an adult dog. As Dunbar notes, there appears to be a "puppy license" of sorts, possession of which entitles you to be an utter pest without much repercussion. Past the age of 4 1/2 months, the "puppy license" expires as hormone levels shift and psychological changes occur. At this point, adult dogs begin to gradually insist on more controlled, respectful interactions from youngsters (Clothier, 2000, p.6).

Brad Crayne

A puppy muzzle punches the adult Great Pyrenees. This pup is still enjoying puppy license, a period when young canids are allowed to practice rude behaviors toward adult canines, including stealing food or bones.

Barbara Handelman

Pan is reaping the benefits of his puppy license when he places his head and neck over Luca's shoulders. The chin over behavior usually signifies sexual interest, as a prelude to riding up or is a sign of one canid wanting to take control of a situation (perhaps he wants Luca's bone). In either case, if Pan were not still at an age when puppy license prevails, Luca would most likely have growled and pinned him to make the point that Pan is being rude. In this instance, Luca simply ignored him.

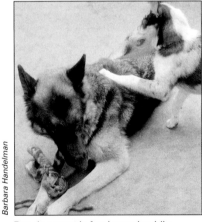

Barbara Handelman

Pan does a rude foreleg stab while showing an agonistic pucker, and flared whiskers. Luca is the portrait of forbearance. He continues to chew his toy, and ignores the pup. Notice his slight head turn and ears turned in opposite directions, suggesting some emotional conflict.

Barbara Handelman

Pan barks rudely in Luca's face. Pan is doing an agonistic pucker with lips wide open in the shape of a "C" suggesting he intends to be making a serious threat. Luca is doing a lying down, paw-lift, and has slightly lowered his head. Such deference is granted only because Pan's puppy license is still in effect. Luca is chewing on the ball in his mouth. Chewing acts as a self-soothing pacifier, increasing Luca's tolerance.

Barbara Handelman

Pan is really pushing the puppy license boundary with the ultimate in rude behavior – he is humping Luca's head!

218

Push Off:

Canids use their feet and legs both offensively (see *Paw Thwacks* and *Foreleg Stabs*) and defensively while engaged in *Ritualized Aggression, play* and all out attacks. One canid can push an "opponent" away, or lift the opponent off his body with force applied upwards with his feet and front or hind legs.

Eight-month-old Great Pyrenees littermates play during a puppy reunion. They are wrestling and the pup on the bottom does a playful push off.

These two playful dogs look like they are performing an acrobatic act. The dog on top has a rounded back which suggests he may be sexually aroused and wanting to mount or ride up on his playmate, who is lying on his back doing a push off to fend off the ride up, while perhaps keeping the game going.

Two wolves engage in intense ritualized aggression. The wolf on top has taken control of the interaction. He does many threat behaviors, including an agonistic pucker, and piloerection evident from the arch of his neck all the way down his tail. He is partially standing on and partially standing over his opponent. Although the wolf on the bottom has taken the submissive position of lying on his back – he is demonstrating submissive-aggression, using all four feet to do a push off, a wide gape, hard eyes, and ears pinned back.

219

Rally:

(Also see *Affiliative Behavior, Greeting Behaviors, Submissive Behaviors*)

A rally occurs when three or more canids gather to enthusiastically greet another animal or human. The greetings may be boisterous, include much licking, *tail wagging*, *pawing*, and some *active submissive behavior* and/or *appeasement behaviors*. "Occasionally aggressive bouts break out when two wolves with a history of *aggression* come together in the rally, or when an *alpha* wolf appears 'fed up' with being the focus of attention" (Klinghammer, 2002, p. 25).

Most people who live in a multi-dog household are familiar with the rally phenomenon. Dogs may rush to the person entering and vie for her attention, by jumping up, whining, *muzzle nudging*, *hip nudging*, and offering some object carried in the canid's mouth.

Monty Sloan

Wolves gather for a rally.

Barbara Handelman

Dogs rally to a familiar person.

Redirected Activity:

"Behaviours that are redirected originate with a specific target but transfer to another target" (Sue Alexander, letter to author, August, 2007).

> Direction of an activity away from the principal target and toward another, less appropriate target. This is usually best identified when the recognized activity is interrupted by less appropriate target or by a third party, and in contrast to displacement activity, redirected activity appears to be a substitution "in kind" of the interrupted behavior (Overall, 2001, p. 3).

Example: A male dog is aroused by a teaser bitch, and redirects his sexual interest to the handler during semen collection.

Redirected Behavior (Also called Remnant Behavior and Ritualized Behavior):

"A behaviour can be said to be redirected when it has lost its original function but has kept a common element of it. The *muzzle nudge* is an example of a *redirected behavior* originating from the act of eliciting regurgitation" (Abrantes, 1997, p. 208).

Examples: *muzzle nudge, appeasement behaviors, pawing,* carrying objects as a *greeting behavior.*

Great Pyrenees puppy does muzzle nudge to Pan, the one-year-old Collie. The muzzle nudge is a remnant of soliciting regurgitation.

Regurgitate:

(Also see *Et-Epimeletic Behavior*)

Wolves and other wild canids carry food from a kill back to their young. A wolf can consume up to twenty percent of his own body weight. It is easier for canids to carry quantities of food in their bellies, over significant distances, than it is to carry a similar quantity of food in their jaws. Stimulated by the pups' nudging his mouth or throat (food begging), a wolf will regurgitate food for the pups to eat (Goodman, Wolf Park Behavior Seminar, 2007).

Puppies gather around an adult wolf begging for food by nudging and pawing at her.

A kitten and her Golden Retriever puppy-friend curl up for a nap together. Companionship seems equally important to them both.

Photo by Rachel Friedman

Section 19: Relaxation Postures

Turning in Place:

Monty Sloan

Canids often circle before lying down. This behavior serves to create a comfortable resting spot.

Back Sleeping:

Seen most often in young dogs, but may extend into adulthood.

Barbara Handelman

An infant puppy, only a few days old, sleeps contentedly on his back against his mother's giant paw, which offers warmth and reassurance.

Barbara Handelman

A Basset Hound relaxes on her back in the midst of other dogs in a day care center, where other dogs are milling around and playing.

223

Curled Resting Posture:

Sprawling Sphinx Rest:

Sprawling Sphinx Sleeping:

Straight Line Sleeping Sphinx:

The Frog Sphinx:

Lateral Reclination:

Irish Wolfhound – that's a lot of sprawl!

Using Pillows:

Louie the Gentle Giant rests contentedly with one of his housemate cats as a pillow.

Two Basenjis sleep in lateral reclination positions with the one on the bottom serving as a comfy pillow.

Even a wolf appreciates a good pillow.

225

Pan, age four-months, enjoys a moment of puppy license, while
doing a ride up on Louie, an adolescent giant dog.

Photo by Barbara Handelman

Section 20:
Reproductive & Sexual Behavior

Reproductive behavior includes any behavior associated with reproduction: courting, mating, denning, whelping, and supportive behavior from other pack members in wolves – or human caregivers in dogs.

In the course of normal play, male puppies as young as five-weeks-old show sexual/reproductive behavior including *mounting* with humping/thrusting. The behavior may become inappropriate and problematic if older puppies try to mount objects, children, or older canids who respond aggressively.

Canids of both genders, neutered or intact, are likely to engage in *mounting* and humping behavior when they are aroused. The source of the arousal may simply be play excitement. *Mounting* may also arise when one animal is attempting to control another, and thus assert *dominance* in that particular situation (also see *ride up*). *Mounting* and humping (also called thrusting) are also essential components of the *motor patterns* involved in copulation.

Courtship:

May include running together, nuzzling, *rubbing under, parallel walking* and other playful behaviors.

- Courtship rub under

- Courtship *head press*

- *Rebuff:*

A female wolf tells her male suitor to back off. An agonistic gape accompanies her lunge toward the male. He is showing avoidance by shifting his weight backwards and to the side.

- Chasing away the competition, a cut off or distance increasing behavior.

Note the lack of rocking horse motion – all forward motion is horizontal with very little vertical movement – this is a serious effort at distance increasing and both wolves know it. Notice the dramatic tail tuck of the wolf being chased.

- Male wolf licking female genitalia

Male wolf on the right licks the female's vulva checking her readiness for mating.

- Male knocking off the competition.

The male wolf in the center knocks off another male wolf who has begun to mount the female.

- Flagging or averting the tail

Female wolf flagging or averting her tail

- *Clasp* as prelude to *mounting*

The male wolf is clasping the female.

Ride Up:

(Also see *T-Formation*)

Dogs ride up just as their canid cousins, the wolves, do. This is a sexualized behavior (expressing sexual drive) that may occur without the motivation to actually copulate. The ride up shares the same motivations as *mounting* and humping when they occur during *social play* interactions.

Female wolf does a ride up as a courtship gesture toward the male who will be her mate.

Monty Sloan

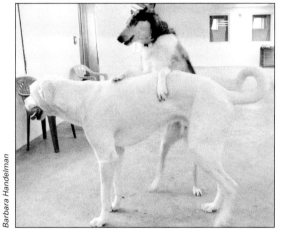

Barbara Handelman

Two male adolescent dogs with sexual arousal occurring during play excitement. A ladder might have been handy!

Mounting • Pelvic Thrusts • Intromission (penile penetration of the vagina):

Monty Sloan

Monty Sloan

229

Copulatory Tie:

The penis swells, due to engorgement with blood, causing an erection. The Bulbus Glandis (at the base of the penis) also swells – with the effect of locking the penis inside the vagina of the female – thus causing the tie. The sperm rich fraction of the semen enters the female within eighty seconds of ejaculation. The tie may continue for as long as an hour. It is not, however, necessary for the pair to remain tied for longer than eighty seconds for insemination to occur.

There is no definitive social/behavioral explanation for the copulatory tie but theories abound. Wolf ethologist, Pat Goodman, (Behavior Seminar Wolf Park, 2007) stated that the tie may facilitate pair bonding and thus enhance the probability of the male's participation in feeding and protecting the pups during the neonatal stage.

Forsythe, Dawkins and others suggest that as long as the male remains tied with the bitch, she cannot mate with another canid – thus the tied male not only has a greater chance of impregnating the bitch but also being the only sire. Given that a male will be fatigued immediately post mating, that is the time when another male might try his luck. Even during the tie, the male or female can fend off other suitors. The tied position is remarkably flexible, and the pair may even squabble with each other while tied – after the male has executed the leg-over maneuver, which results in the two still being attached but able to turn and face each other or another canid.

The male wolf on the left has just completed swinging his hind leg over the back of the female, so that now they can maneuver together – even though they are still tied – they can face each other or together fend off competing suitors.

Washing Up After Intromission:

The canids mate, wash up afterwards and then repeat the act of copulation. Multiple matings mean more chances for sperm to survive.

Attend:

A behavior that happens only during the breeding season when one mate stays constantly in the same vicinity as the other member of the mated pair.

Attending after copulation was described by Pat Goodman (Wolf Park Behavior Seminar, 2007) as a part of "courtship when the wolves seem attached by a bungee cord between them – that only extends a limited distance."

Denning:

Male stands over his mate, to protect his breeding rights, and in furtherance of their bonding.

These wolves are digging a shelter, perhaps creating a den for pups.

Moon, age 10 months, stands over his life-long friend and training buddy, Willow. They were taking a quiet, companionable moment between bouts of rough and tumble play.

Photo by Barbara Handelman

Section 21:
Resource Guarding – Stereotypic Behaviors

Resource Guarding:

(See *Resource Guarding Aggression*)

Ritualization:

(Also see *Metasignals*)

The evolution of social signals.

> Ritualized behaviors include a wide variety of fixed action patterns, such as flagging in a bitch to indicate readiness to mate – Flagging is an instinctual behavior, triggered by hormonal receptivity, and a male engaged in courting. Males receiving the flagging signal understand the meaning, also instinctually, which allows the bitch and dog to be ready to mate at the same time – in synchronicity (Sue Alexander, letter to author, September, 2007).

> Ritualization is the evolutionary process whereby a signal behavior is established or improved in such a way that it becomes a more effective or efficient means of communication. Any attribute of an animal upon which natural selection can act – behavioral, physiological, developmental, or morphological traits – can be the basis of a communicative signal.

> The key attribute of the trait is that it in some way conveys information, usually about one individual to another. This information then makes the world of the recipient more predictable, less chaotic (Greenberg, 2005).

Monty Sloan

The female wolf, on the right, is averting her tail, also called flagging, which is a ritualized behavior that is part of the mating, fixed action pattern.

233

Rolling:

(Also see *Scent Rolling*)

Rolling serves many purposes for canids – they may mark an area, pick up scent, scratch a part of their bodies they cannot reach, or they may just roll for fun.

Some dogs roll to interrupt group play to slow down their own and their playmates' heightening arousal levels.

Louie is rolling for the pure pleasure of it.

The Great Dane rolls to interrupt play arousal.

Few canids can resist rolling in putrid carrion, or scents left on the ground by another species of animal (such as skunk spray).

Scent rolling wolf.

Scent Rolling:

Scent rolling is a communication behavior – "Wolves carry the scent of prey back to the pack. Scent gives information about health and location of the prey to other pack members" (Goodman, Wolf Park Behavior Seminar, 2007). Scent rolling in domestic dogs is an example of a ritualized behavior that remains in the dogs' behavioral repertoire even though it is no longer relevant to their evolutionary success.

Wolf scent rolling.

Rub On:

"To press against and slide along a companion or an object, such as a fence or a tree. May be performed as a method of grooming, especially when shedding the coat in the spring. May precede scent rolling" (Goodman, et al., 2002, p. 27).

Monty Sloan

Wolf on the left rubs his head on the chest of supine wolf.

Scoot:

(Also see *Epimeletic Behavior*)

Scooting is a personal grooming behavior most often performed after defecation. The canid sits, and, maintaining the sit, lifts its hind legs slightly and uses its forelegs to walk a few steps forward. This drags its rump along the ground, giving the anal area a good rub. It may be used after excreting a runny stool, which may help clean the fur if any diarrhea clung to it. After a lot of straining to defecate, canids may scoot as if to relieve irritation. They will sometimes whirl and lick or nibble groom their anal area as if suddenly experiencing a particularly urgent itch. They may scoot after licking and nibbling or intersperse scooting with licking and nibbling. Possibly this behavior could aid in expressing anal sacs, but we are so far unable to confirm this with certainty (Goodman, et al., 2002).

Monty Sloan

A wolf scoots along the grass. Dog perform this behavior for the same reasons wolves do.

235

Scratching:

(Also see *Displacement Behavior*)

Scratching is often seen as a calming signal. But it is also well recognized and studied as a *displacement behavior*. It may be a signal to other dogs that helps both the scratcher and the dogs in view of the scratching become calmer. Scratching may also serve as a way for a dog to interrupt or slow down escalating play arousal. Of course, sometimes dogs scratch simply because they have an itch. One can usually tell the difference by the location of the scratching. If the canid scratches just the shoulder with a dropped opposite elbow, it is a *displacement behavior* – if the scratching is elsewhere or moves around, it is likely an itch.

Scratching as a displacement behavior happened in this instance when play arousal was peaking. Note that the Collie's piloerector reflex conveys that he is also feeling aroused. The dogs may feel uncertain about how to avoid reactive aggression. Scratching serves to interrupt and diffuse the arousal levels.

Self-Control:

Dogs employ self-control behaviors. Some are trained behaviors while others are innate. Self control is an important survival skill in wild canids. Pounce too soon and lunch gets away!

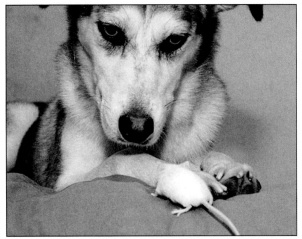

This dog watches the live mouse with great interest, and imposes tremendous self-control over any predatory responses.

There are treats lined up on both forelegs, Pan ignores the food while maintaining eye contact with his person.

Self-Handicapping and Role Reversing Behaviors:

Canids use self-handicapping behaviors to improve the likelihood of calm, non-threatening canid to canid interactions. Self-handicapping is especially relevant when big canids play with small canids, or healthy adult canids play with puppies or elderly dogs. The larger or older canids will assume positions, or employ play techniques that "level the playing field", in order not to overwhelm the smaller or younger dogs or older but weaker dogs, and to keep their play mates involved in the play interaction. According to Marc Bekoff, "self-handicapping behaviors serve to reduce asymmetries between the interacting animals and foster the reciprocity that it needed for play to occur." Bekoff continues:

Self-handicapping happens when an individual performs a behaviour pattern that might compromise herself. For example a coyote might not bite her play partner as hard as she can, or she might not play as vigorously as she can.

...Role-reversing occurs when a dominant animal performs an action during play that would not normally occur during real aggression. For example a dominant animal might not voluntarily roll over on his back during fighting, but would do so while playing. In some instances role-reversing and self-handicapping might occur together. For example, a dominant individual might roll over while playing with a subordinate animal and inhibit the intensity of a bite. From a functional perspective, self-handicapping and role-reversing, similar to using specific play invitation signals or altering behavioural sequences, might serve to signal an individual's intention to continue to play (Bekoff, 2001, p. 83-84).

Self-handicapping is a defining component of play. Self-handicapping is an evolutionary stable strategy to ensure that young members of a pack of canids can survive to pass on their genes. The doggy hand-me-down through the generations applies this trait to young and old, smaller and weaker individuals (Sue Alexander, letter to author, September, 2007).

Barbara Handelman

Note that Moon, the Aussie, holds the tug toy lightly with his front teeth only, while Luca, the very young puppy, has gripped the toy with a full mouth bite. Moon also offers a paw-lift to convey his lack of threatening intent.

Barbara Handelman

Luca, as an adult, returns the self-handicapping favor during this game of tug with Pan, age three-months.

Barbara Handelman

Wargas, the Anatolian Shepherd, (on left) while still an adolescent, stands 34 inches tall and weighs 120 pounds. During a bout of jaw sparring, he lies down to level the playing field with the Collie, who is 24 1/2 inches tall and weighs in at 68 pounds.

Separation Anxiety:

When animals exhibit symptoms of anxiety or excessive distress when they are left alone, the condition is called separation anxiety; however, the most commonly exhibited behaviours (elimination, destruction, excessive vocalization) are only the most visible signs of anxiety. Drooling, panting, and cognitive signs of anxiety will not be diagnosed but probably occur (Overall, 2001, p. 4).

Shake Off:

Shaking-off is often a *displacement signal*. A shake off may serve to calm the dog who is shaking or others around him. A shake off often follows some form of uncomfortable encounter, or physical handling with which the canid is not pleased. All canids will *shake off* to rid their coats of water or snow.

Barbara Handelman

Cary, the tricolor Collie, does a shake off after an uncomfortable encounter with another dog. His lush coat makes the shake off appear very dramatic.

Kevin Peuhkurinen

When an Irish Wolfhound does a shake-off to rid his coat of water after a swim, everything around him is drenched. Who needs a sprinkler system?

Monty Sloan

Shake off sequence: Wolf on the left threatens – the other wolf does a shake off moments later.

Slow Downs:

(Also see *Self-Control Behaviors*)

Slow downs are behaviors intended to interrupt rising play arousal before it escalates into *aggressive behavior*.

Examples: Lying down, *rolling, bowing, sniffing*, stopping to take a drink.

Stopping play to take a drink is a slow down behavior that may have little to do with thirst. Note piloerection.

Lying down during a social play interaction may also serve as a slow down behavior.

Sneeze:

(Also see *Stress Behavior*)

Some canids sneeze as an *indicator of stress*. Other times, sneezing can be a sign of pleasure, or of heightened excitement. Some canids sneeze to emphasize annoyance or when frustrated.

Sneezing is sometimes considered a suppressed bark, in a stressed or conflicted canid. Of course, sometimes canids sneeze because something has tickled their nasal passages.

Sniffing:

(Also see *Greeting Behaviors, Displacement Behaviors, Calming Signals*)

All canids can glean untold amounts of knowledge about their surroundings and the inhabitants through their olfactory senses. Canids sniff as part of *greeting behaviors*.

Sniffing can also serve as a calming signal or *displacement behavior* or as a means to slow down escalating arousal levels during group play sessions. Sniffing serves as a slow down behavior when canids suddenly stop to closely examine a spot of ground with their noses, when they might, moments earlier, have passed over the same spot with no interest at all.

Sniffing as greeting.

Sniffing as greeting.

Sniffing as displacement behavior during raucous play.

Sniffing as displacement behavior.

Snow Plow:

Canids will explore the area beneath blankets of newly fallen snow. They use their noses as if their heads were a snowplow: nose to the ground. When they are moving, the broad area of the skull forces a path through the snow.

Canids explore for familiar and new scents that have been hidden by the snow. They may also be searching for small prey such as voles, moles, and mice that build winter trails under the snow. For some canids, "snow plowing" appears motivated by pleasure. Those canids appear to be having fun as they plow excitedly through the snow.

Barbara Handelman

Doing a snow plow, Moon explores in the newly fallen, deep snow.

Monty Sloan

A wolf does a snow plow searching for scents that have been hidden by the deep snow.

Social Hierarchies (Also Called Dominance Hierarchies):

(Also see *Dominance*, *Submission*)

There is considerable controversy related to the idea of humans in dominance hierarchies with dogs. Domestic dogs are not pack animals in the same ways as wild wolves, or even captive wolves. Some feral dogs live in loosely structured groups.

> However, in multidog households, even when a dominant-subordinate relationship clearly exists as shown by ritualized displays over valued resources, lower-ranking dogs do not routinely greet high-ranking dogs in a manner that displays rank. In addition the postures that dogs can show vary by breed. Moore paedomorphic breeds (those resembling the juvenile stages of wolf development), such as Cavalier King Charles spaniel, have a smaller communicative repertoire than breeds that physically resemble adult wolves. (Yin, 2007, p. 416)

To date, no scientific research has tested the most popular theories related to dogs and dominance, and yet, almost every negative behavioral trait has been attributed to dominance by one or another trainer or self-proclaimed canine behaviorist. It has yet to be proven that dogs living in multi-dog households form a rigid, linear pack with each other or with their humans.

The human/dog pack hierarchy debate was fueled by early research about wolves in the wild. That research has since been proven to be based on insufficient and inaccurate research (Mech 1999, p. 1197). More recently, observations of captive wolves have been used as models for postulating about domestic dogs' social hierarchies.

David Mech, wolf ethologist, stated that one cannot extrapolate accurate information about wild wolves by studying captive wolves – the logic is equally faulty when theorists apply information about captive wolves to domestic dogs:

> Attempting to apply information about the behavior of assemblages of unrelated captive wolves to the familial structure of natural packs has resulted in considerable confusion. Such an approach is analogous to trying to draw inferences about human family dynamics by studying humans in refuge camps (Mech, 1979, p.1198).

Social hierarchies among wild wolves serve several purposes. First and foremost, they determine breeding rights, then allocation of resources (who gets to eat first and most), who gets the prized sleeping spots, etc. Some of the time wolf packs hunt together, especially when hunting prey animals larger than themselves – thus the pack members work cooperatively for the procurement of food. The pack also helps feed and look out for the young of the breeding pair. Once they reach sexual maturity, most young male wolves leave the pack, and if they are lucky, they find a mate of their own, with whom they start a new pack. If they are successful, they become the alpha of that pack, regardless of what their status had been in their pack of origin.

No scientific research has ever been performed or attempted regarding dog-to-dog dominance theories related to dogs living in human households. Nor have research studies examined the relevance of dominance theories in human social interactions or training with dogs.

> It is important to realize that an actual dominance-submission relationship exists only when one individual consistently submits to the other.... In most stable relationships, the submissive individual automatically defers to the dominant individual in the absence of threatening posture by the dominant individual..... people who rely on dominance to train their dogs may need to regularly threaten them with aggressive displays or repeatedly use physical force. It is important to be aware that even when an individual can clearly establish dominance over another, in many species, a dominant rank within a group is often relatively short lived....

> High rank is repeatedly tested and can be maintained only as long as the top ranking individual is physically strong enough to win the aggressive encounters. Thus people may not be able to retain their rank. In a family, children and elderly people can rarely establish high rank through force and are especially at risk of being injured if they attempt to do so (Yin, 2007, p. 417)

Socialization:

(Also see *Classical Conditioning, Flooding*)

Socialization is a systematic process of exposing a pup to a wide range of dogs, people, and places. There is a fairly narrow window for proper socialization of puppies, that ends when the pup is approximately twenty weeks old. The length of the time varies with breeds and with individual puppies. The structured process should begin during the early weeks in the whelping box and continue during the first twenty weeks of his life. Through socialization with dogs of all ages, and people of every description, pups learn the requisite communication skills essential for understanding both humans and *conspecifics* and how to resolve conflicts without biting or fighting.

Socialization includes exposure to a wide range of social contexts (play with age mates, gentle older canids, and introduction to animals of other species he will likely encounter throughout his life, such as cats, horses, birds, squirrels, etc.)

Socialization should be gradual, voluntary, and paced in accordance with the puppy's individual *temperament*. Some pups will take longer than others to habituate to unusual or loud sounds, strange footing, objects that flap or thump. There is much that can be done, even while puppies are still with their mothers, to introduce them to unusual sights and sounds. For example, commercially produced audio tapes are available with the sounds of everything from vacuum cleaners and thunderstorms to crowds of people, and fireworks. Carpet samples with various textures, sand painted wood, tile flooring, and a metal grate might be placed on the floor of the whelping box for pups to experience underfoot, once their eyes are open and they are walking.

To understand the importance of socialization, compare it to creating a solid foundation to support a tall building. Once the foundation is properly laid, the building will likely withstand the test of time, storms and earthquakes. Without a solid foundation, the best building materials – training in the case of dogs – may not hold up under the stress of new sights, sounds, unusual footing, or people in unusual costumes.

Many people confuse socialization with socializing. Socializing with an occasional visiting dog in the pup's home, or local environment ,is not enough. Taking a young puppy to a dog park, turning it loose to be approached by bully dogs, and pushy puppies – would qualify as socializing, not socialization.

For puppies, unstructured exposure to intense stimuli is likely to result in *flooding*. Instead of habituating to new experiences, the pup becomes over stimulated and overwhelmed. If a pup shows signs of stress during a socialization activity, the activity should end, and be approached again more gradually when the pup is a bit older.

Classical conditioning to desensitize a pup to objects or environmental structures, such as stairs, that frighten pups, is not usually the best option for reducing or eliminating *fear*. Even the slightest mistiming of a click or other reinforcement, risks pairing a positive reward with a fearful response. As a result, the pup may always associate the specific circumstances that produced the reward with feeling fearful.

Maintaining a dog's socialization is a lifelong process. Just as one might check for cracks in a building's foundation so must socialization be practiced and reinforced over the course of the dog's lifetime. He will then remain accustomed to adapting to unusual sights, sounds, people of all descriptions, and unfamiliar environments.

Soft Curves:

Canids who have friendly intent during greetings may approach each other with distinct curving lines in their body posture. Curves convey non-threatening intentions.

Louie is a portrait of curving body lines.

Sparring:

(See *Clasping* and *Jaw Wrestling*)

Spatulate Tongue:

Spatulate tongue occurs particularly when a dog is stressed, but may also occur if the dog is hyperthermic/ overheatead and panting heavily to cool down his whole body. To determine the cause, note others signs of stress. In this dog, *tension ridges* in his face as well as *whale eye* and forward *flared whiskers* suggest that this spatulate tongue portrays stress.

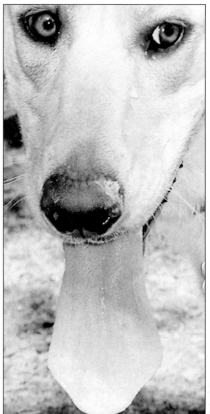

This dog displays an example of a spatulate tongue.

Splitting:

(Also see *Distance Increasing Signals*)

Splitting can be seen when one canid moves between two or more other canids, creating physical distance between the other animals. Splitting is clearly purposeful and intentional behavior. Some canids do not take kindly to being split away from an interaction of interest to them, and may respond with *aggressive behavior*. Most canids respond to splitting by moving away, at least temporarily. Some of the purposes of splitting:

- To diffuse tension between canids in the group

- To isolate one canid for sexual advances

- To isolate a canid for exclusive one-on-one play

- To isolate the canid who has become "prey" in a *predatory play* interaction

Split occurring in a social play interaction. Wolves have play faces and look generally relaxed.

A split used to interrupt tension between the wolves on the right and left.

A split used during predatory play interaction, or perhaps to signal a change in the prey/predator roles.

A split used to isolate dog on left for one-on-one play session.

Squash:

"To sit or lie on a wolf after it has been pinned or knocked down. Unsuspecting wolves at rest may also be squashed" (Goodman, et al., 2002, p. 31).

Standing On:

Standing on, sitting on, dragging feet over the body of another animal is a rudely provocative behavior, likely to escalate an interaction to the next level of intensity in *ritualized aggression.*

Wolf on the left is standing over the other wolf who is doing a push off.

Standing Over:

Standing over can have several different meanings discerned by observing contextual and postural clues and other behaviors happening concurrently. Males may stand over their mates as a way of attending their mate during breeding season, thus preventing a rebreeding by a "sneaker male". Standing over may also be provocative *testing* behavior, where one canid stands over another to see if he can provoke the other into standing up. In some instances, standing over may be a dominant posture that precedes *ritualized aggressive behavior*. Standing over also occurs during *courtship* and other companionable moments.

Standing over during a companionable moment between siblings.

Standing over as a provocative act about which the wolf on the bottom is not pleased.

Standing Tall:

(Also see *Height Seeking*)

During an interaction, one canid pulls himself up to full height. The neck is arched and the ears are forward and alert. The individual "standing tall" may stare at another canid, in an effort to intimidate him or her. If the tail is not naturally carried high, it may rise while the animal is standing tall. Some canids stand well up on their toes, almost as if standing on tip toe, in order to maximize the appearance of greatest size. The behavior is sometimes seen during *courtship,* but is most often part of a threat display. The effect may be enhanced by *piloerection*.

Louie is standing tall, a dominance posture in this instance.

Collie is standing tall as part of a display of sexual interest.

Barbara Handelman

Border Collie is standing nearly on tip toe. He is irritated with the Collie's persistent advances, and ready to warn him to back off.

Stereotypic Behavior (Also Called Stereotypies):

Stereotypy: a repetitious, relatively unvaried sequence of movements that have no obvious purpose or function, but that are usually derived from contextually normal maintenance behaviours (e.g., grooming, eating, walking) (Overall, 2001, p. 3).

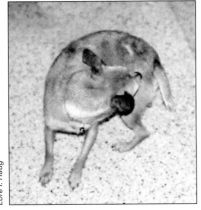

Lore I. Haug

Tail Chasing/Self-Mutilation

Lore I. Haug

Geophagia, eating dirt compulsively

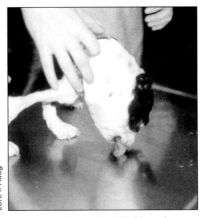

Lore I. Haug

Compulsive Stereotypic Licking of any substrate or other smooth surface.

Compulsive disorders are also apparently pointless behaviors that occur to a degree that they interfere with normal functioning. In humans these behaviors serve to reduce the anxiety produced by the obsession. We do not know if animals have obsessions, so we cannot say with certainty that compulsions serve that purpose in animals. Compulsive behaviors are not always stereotypic. For example, a dog might compulsively stare into space. Staring is not a repetitive behavior (which is the hallmark of a stereotypy). Some compulsions are stereotyped; they would therefore be categorized as both a stereotypy and a compulsion (Lore Haug, letter to author, January, 2008).

The dog human relationship is arguably the closest we humans can ever get to establishing a dialogue with another sentinel life form, so it is not surprising that people tend to emerge from such encounters with a special affinity for man's best friend.

— James Serpell

This German Short Haired Pointer displays lip licking and flared whiskers. He is moving quickly to his right to avoid a life-size, stuffed, toy dog.
Photo by Barbara Handelman

Section 22: Stress

Stress:

(Also see *Distress* and *Eustress*)

It can manifest in every aspect of life, in every situation and also at every age. The perception of stress, as well as the coping strategies developed by the organism, can be different from human to human and also among dogs. For example, different dogs experiencing the same situation perceive it differently, some not seeing it as stressful at all, while others are clearly stressed by it. Completely different symptoms and coping strategies can be seen among those that show stress reaction (Scholz and Reinhardt, 2007, p. 9).

Not All Stress is Negative:

Fear, excitement, anxiety, playful, sexual, and aggressive arousal are all closely related. Duration of the feeling state, and environmental factors can cause arousal to increase. What starts as pleasure may transform into *fear* or *aggression*.

Responses to both positive and negative stressors share some of the same characteristics and appearance. They also cause some of the same neurochemical changes in the brain.

The concurrent appearance of two or more displays of moderate stress combine to indicate extreme/severe stress.

Indicators of Mild Stress:

- Blinking
- Lip licking
- Paw-lift

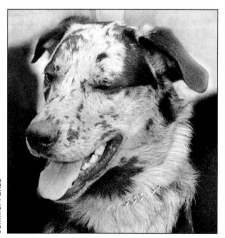

Jennifer Parizo

Barbara Handelman

Jennifer Parizo

- Licking and mouthing

- Pulling back

- Scratching

- Shaking off

- Sneezing

- Stretching

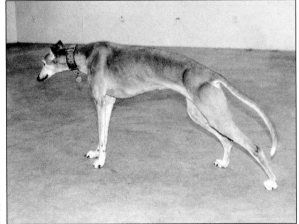

- Yawning

Indicators of Moderate Stress:

- Cautious/Reluctant to Approach

- Tail lowered

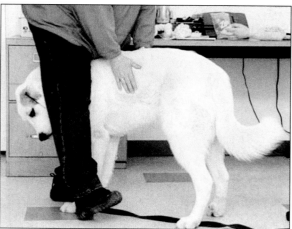

- Tongue Flicks

- Lumpy Whisker Bed (may precede *flared whiskers* or *agonistic pucker*)

Beware of still water, a still dog, and a still enemy.

– Yiddish Proverb

Indicators of Extreme or Severe Stress:

- Arched back

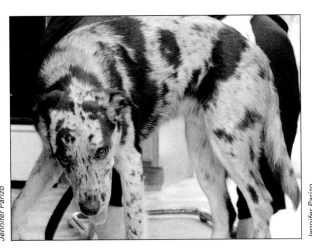

- Dilating Pupils

- Ears Forced Back
- Whale Eye

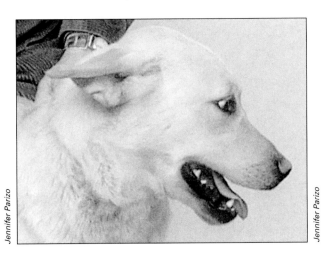

- Facial Tension Ridges

- Full Body Stiffness

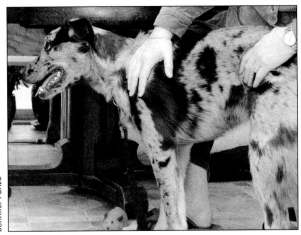

- Hard eyes

- Heavy Panting with Drooling

Sabarika

- Pinched Ear

Lore I. Haug

- Shedding Hair and Dander

Barbara Handelman

- Skin Drawn Tightly on Head

Lynn Crook

- Stiff or Braced Legs

Barbara Handelman

- Sweaty Paws

Barbara Handelman

The only sweat glands dog have are in their paws. Wolves do not sweat even from their feet.

- Tail Tucked

- Trembling
- "Whale eye"

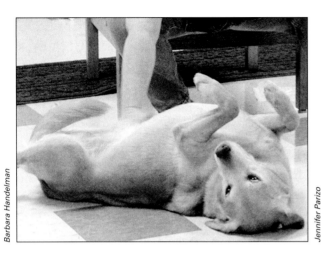

Barbara Handelman

Jennifer Parizo

- Whiskers Flared

Lynn Crook

Monty Sloan

The wolf in the foreground grasps the neck of the wolf in the background. The wolf being grabbed has his whiskers flared forward and is doing a tongue flick.

God sat down for a moment when the dog was finished in order to watch it... and to know that it was good, that nothing was lacking, that it could not have been made better.

— Rainer Marie Rilke

Anyone who has accustomed himself to regard the life of any living creature as worthless is in danger of arriving also at the idea of worthless human lives.

— Albert Schweitzer

*We listened for a voice
crying in the wilderness.*

*And we heard the
jubilation of wolves!*

— Durwood L. Allen

A wolf does a stretch of a single hind leg while standing on a log.

Photo by Monty Sloan

Section 23: Stretching – T-Formation

Stretching:

Stretching takes many forms and may express a range of feelings. Stretching in a *bowing* posture may be a play invitation. Stretching may also be a *displacement behavior*, especially when combined with other signals directed at calming others. Stretching also relieves physical tension in the canid doing the stretching, and may occur when tired, or when just rising after sleep.

Foreleg stretch or bow.

Hind leg stretch, both legs.

259

Submission

In Ethology, submission is generally defined as the yielding of a subordinate to a more dominant member of a hierarchy.

As a strategy, submissive behavior may benefit the canid in several ways – he may avoid the risk of injury during a fight; he may be able to take a less risky role during group hunting; and he may obtain the opportunity to have access to resources by the association formed with a more dominant member of the hierarchy (Sue Alexander, letter to author, September 2007).

Submissive-Aggressive Behavior:

(See *Aggressive Behavior* Categories)

Active Submission:

Submission initiated by a canid soliciting interaction with a higher-ranking animal. Active submission is distinguished from confident greetings by the *crouching* posture and tucked tail and flattened ears.

"Active submission occurs as a normal greeting behavior between dogs and humans" (Haug, letter to the author, April 2, 2007).

Examples: *submissive grin*, puppy licking, *crouching*, groveling, tail might be wagging or tucked; *ears are flattened*, might *paw* at the other dog's face.

Active submissive displays include tongue flick, tail tuck, crouch, and piloerection.

Active submissive displays include turning the back to other wolf, crouch, tail tuck, head turn, and submissive grin.

Obnoxious Submission:

(Also see *Appeasement*)

Dogs also display obnoxious submission in their interactions with other dogs and with humans. In a *social play* situation, some dogs interact only by offering submissive and *appeasement* behaviors including, but not limited to, *rolling* on the ground, *submissive urination*, effusive licking, hip nudging and other active submissive behaviors that preclude another dog from actually interacting with them. The potential playmate cannot interrupt the submissive behavior barrage.

Obnoxious submission may confer some sort of evolutionary advantage to the submissive dog or might be a by-product of artificially selected traits. In the wild, a dominant wolf may relinquish food or other resources to a subordinate, just to relieve himself of the annoyance of being the recipient of so much obnoxious submissive behavior.

Some dogs are so effusive in their greetings to humans that the person may feel overwhelmed or annoyed by the dog's persistent body wiggles, squirming while being petted, *rolling* around at their feet, repetitive hip nudging, and *submissive urination*. Dogs being rehabilitated after a history of an abusive relationship with a former owner, may use obnoxious submission with new caretakers. Some abused dogs generalize the abusive experience to include all new people they meet – thus their submissive greetings may seem excessive or obnoxious.

Monty Sloan

Wolfgang (in the foreground), a Beta wolf, is being positively obsequious in his submissive displays towards Tristan, the Alpha of the pack.

Lynn Crook

These four photographs are of the same two dogs interacting on three separate occasions. Clearly, there is a pattern of obnoxious submissive by the black and white dog and varying degrees of tolerance on the part of the brown dog. Finally, the brown dog makes it clear that "enough is enough".

Passive Submission:

Passive submission is a distance increasing signal, whereas active submission is distance decreasing behavior.

Examples: the canid rolls over onto his side or back, presenting belly up to another canid, submissive urination, inguinal presentation. There is no attempt to greet or appease the other dog; tail may be tucked, ears are flattened.

Monty Sloan

The two wolves in the background are standing over the wolf who has assumed the passive submissive position – rolled over onto his back. The wolf in the foreground sits on the passively submitting wolf who rolled onto his back.

Monty Sloan

The wolf on the left is in a classic passive submissive posture, lying on his back showing his underbelly, while the standing wolf displays dominant postures including ears forward, tail raised, and piloerection.

Submissive Grin:

Pan does a bow, with his ears back, while doing a submissive grin toward Louie, who is standing in a confident posture with his head held high.

Wolf on the left lies partially on his back – he is pawing while displaying a submissive grin toward the wolf who is standing over him.

Submissive Urination:

Some puppies as well as older dogs will urinate as part of a collective display of submissive behaviors. The urination may range from a tiny tinkle on your shoes to the complete loss of bladder control.

T-Formation:

(Also see *Ride Up*)

One Canid approaches the shoulder region of another. Contact is usually made "head on" with the second animal's nose touching the body of the other. Sometimes, especially during *courtship*, one canid may back up so that her rump is facing the other canid's shoulder. If viewed from above, the two canids would be seen forming the shape of the capital letter "T". The canid whose approach forms the stem of the "T" is usually the aggressor. However, an especially confident dog might intentionally take the position at the top of the "T".

A male canid might approach a bitch in estrus in the stem position of the T-formation. If two males are meeting in the T-formation, the canid in the "stem" position might ride up on the other (Goodman, et al., 2002).

Bronte and Pan execute T-formation during play.

Female wolf in estrus backs up to her mate, as part of a courting gesture. Together they create a T-formation.

This dog is doing a dramatic tongue flick. We can't know whether the amplitude of the signal is increased by his desire to lick away water dripping from his coat, or if it is all about conveying his message to another dog.

Photo by Marco De Kloet

Section 24:
Tail Chasing – Umwelt

Tail Chasing:

Tail chasing may be a form of *displacement behavior* in which the dog engages when he does not know what else to do. Often tail chasing is symptomatic of obsessive compulsive tendencies, or *stereotypic behavior*, especially if it occurs frequently and with intensity, or self-injury. Displacement behaviors may also be a sign of conflict – not merely that the dog doesn't know what to do, but also that the dog may feel pressure to engage in a behavior not of his choosing or liking.

Border Collie chasing his tail. In this unusual instance, tail chasing is a trained behavior.

Tail Wagging:

Tail wagging is most often seen as an indicator of a dog's *affiliative* desire to interact socially. Tail wagging may also occur preceding an aggressive attack, or in the company of other submissive *greeting behaviors*. There are many theories relating to the meaning of tail wagging. A study describing the phenomenon, "Asymmetric Tail-Wagging Responses by Dogs to Different Emotive Stimuli," appeared in the March 20, 2007 issue of *Current Biology*. Reporting on this study, Sandra Blakeslee notes:

> Thus when dogs were attracted to something, including a benign, approachable cat, their tails wagged right, and when they were fearful, their tails went left, Dr. Vallortigara said. It suggests that the muscles in the right side of the tail reflect positive emotions while the muscles in the left side express negative ones.

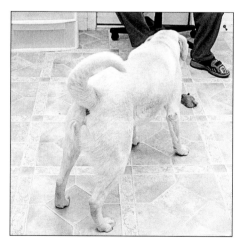

Tail wagging in a circle

Interpretation of tail wagging behavior varies within the scientific community and among dogs themselves. The only tail wagging behavior that

265

seems to reliably predict friendliness is a relaxed tail waving in a circular motion. The role of tail wagging when dogs meet is not completely understood, but may serve to distribute odors for recognition. It may also function as a visual cue signaling peaceful intentions (Fox and Bekoff, 1975, as cited in Blackshaw, 2003).

"Tail-wagging is a context-specific behaviour, which signals excitability or stimulation, such as friendliness/confidence, anxiousness/nervousness and even a threat of aggressive behavior" (Serpell, 1995, p. 119).

Tame:

(Also see *Flight Distance*)

In order for an animal to be considered tame, it must have a *flight distance* of zero. An individual animal may be tamed over the course of its own lifetime. Domestication occurs over many generations.

"Raised and cared for by people" (Coppinger, 2001, p. 63)

> Unlike the wolf, many dogs show not the least wariness towards strange people, and immediately accept them, showing passive and active submission behaviour. This type of dog – its temperament and general demeanor – certainly resembles that of a five-week-old puppy or wolf-cub trustingly accepting all comers. It is not inconceivable that this behavioural paedomorphosis, or perpetuation of infantile behaviour patterns into adulthood, and the absence of fear of strangers, are the result of generations of domestication.

> ...In summary, taming essentially involves socialization, where the animal develops an attachment or social bond with its handler. This can best be accomplished by hand-rearing the wolf, prior to opening its eyes. Individual wolves differ in their later acceptance of strangers, even when they have been given some degree of handling and exposure to various novel stimuli in different situations. The degree of tameness, in terms of emotional stability, also varies from wolf to wolf. In spite of being well-socialized, some wolves remain very wary of strangers and especially of unfamiliar stimuli, and retain the wild temperament in spite of the most careful handling during early development (Fox, 1971, p. 154).

Barbara Handelman

Monty Sloan, Wolf Park Photographer, and Wolfgang enjoy a relationship based on mutual respect and trust. Wolfgang has assumed a submissive posture, while he enjoys a tummy rub.

"What does that mean – tame?"

"It's an act too often neglected," said the fox. "It means to establish ties... Just that," said the fox. "To me, you're still nothing more than a little boy who's just like a hundred thousand other little boys. And I have no need of you. And you, on your part, have no need of me. To you I'm nothing more than a fox like a hundred thousand other foxes. But if you tame me, then we shall need each other. To me, you'll be unique in all the world. To you, I shall be unique in all the world ..."

"What must I do, to tame you?" asked the little prince.

"You must be very patient," replied the fox. "First you'll sit down at a little distance from me – like that – in the grass. I shall look at you out of the corner of my eye, and you will say nothing. Words are the source of misunderstandings. But you'll sit a little closer to me, every day" (St. Exupery, 1943, Ch. 21).

Taxonomy:

Taxonomy is the study of the systematic organization of living things and how they relate to one another.

Taxonomic Classification:

There are many ways to classify living things but the most common is a tree consisting of the following:

Kingdom: *Animalia*

Phylum: *Chordata*

Class: *Mammalia*

Order: *Carnivora*

Family: *Canidae*

Temperament:

The dog's innate individual personality – includes his attitude toward people, dogs and his environment. It also considers his ability to cope with arousal, aggressive approaches from other dogs, and the stress of new sights, sounds, smells, and substrates in the environment.

Dogs are highly capable of adapting to new environments and learning to perform different behaviour in certain situations. However, some aspects of a dog's behaviour might have limited plasticity. In fact if you observe dogs and are focused on behavioural stability, you might find the dog quite consistent in a range of situations. For example, the dog's strategy when meeting unfamiliar persons may be very similar in different contexts and over long periods of time. A dog that shows signs of fear when exposed to loud and strange noise may still, several years later, show similar tendencies in such situations. Other examples are a dog's typical tendency to get excited or to be aggressive. Such stable dispositions create what could be called the behavioural style of a dog, which has also been referred to as temperament, individuality, coping style, behavioural syndromes, and more lately, as animal personality (Svartberg, 2007, p. 182).

Few controlled scientific studies of temperament evaluations exists. The longitudinal accuracy of early temperament evaluation results – in predicting the behavioral profile of puppies and dogs after placement in homes – is difficult to assess. Too many factors come into play when one tries to follow large numbers of puppies from birth through adulthood. Early trauma, abuse, lack of consistent positive training; poor or inadequate nutrition (having to compete for food and shelter resources); re-homing or abandonment – due to human relocation, or intolerance of the dog's behavioral issues – all come into play in the formation of the adult dog's coping styles.

A study by Goddard and Beilharz (1986) which was carried out in order to predict fearfulness, activity and trainability in potential guide dogs, suggested that fearfulness was stable from 8 weeks of age. However, the correlation with adult general fearfulness increased with test age: better predictions were made at higher ages.

Screening of puppies and adult dogs by shelters leads to pre-adoption rehabilitation, and successful placements. A successful placement might be defined by the dog remaining in a single home for the remainder of its life.

Adoption Screening: Matching pets to an appropriate adopter is a crucial aspect of successful re-homing. Adopters must be fully aware of the problem they will be managing and capable of following treatment guidelines. The adoption counselor must also be adept at matching people with the type of pet that they want. A person who is a great canidate for managing a particular problem likely won't be successful if they don't feel a connection with their pet (which is often based on the pet's physical characteristics as well as personality) (Segurson, October, 2007).

Careful evaluation of puppies and dogs as canidates for specific canine careers substantially enhances the dog's probability of completing training and entering the workforce in the career for which it is chosen.

Experienced evaluators and trainers already know many of the attributes adult dogs need in order to enjoy longevity in such careers as guides for the blind, assistance for people with mental or physical disabilities, search and rescue, and law enforcement. However, even those puppies that are bred specifically for working careers and are screened before entering training have less than a fifty-percent chance of successfully joining the workforce as assistance dogs. Without careful screening and on-going *temperament*/behavioral evaluation, the success rate would be much lower.

Whether selecting a puppy from a breeder or an older dog from a shelter, temperament/behavioral evaluations do help screen for the requisite traits working careers demand. Puppies destined for pet homes may be rehabilitated to the point where shyness, sound sensitivity, mild *resource guarding*, and other problematic personality traits would not interfere with the pup's living a healthy, happy, and safe life with the right family. However, assistance dogs, in particular, should not be rehabilitation projects.

To perform confidently – without the long-term health consequences of chronic stress, assistance dogs must possess comfort with and curiosity about new people, places, noises, smells, and substrates (footing). They must have great "bounce back" (recovery from being startled) and respond with curiosity to samples of the inevitable surprises they will face in the world they travel with a disabled handler.

Dee Ganley explains how she has used temperament evaluations with shelter dogs and breeders' litters of puppies:

> Temperament evaluations give us a picture of a puppy/dog's emotional view of the world. Some of what we see is genetic and some of it is learned. Some of it can be modified with positive reinforcement training; some of it will always require management.
>
> How puppies/dogs score is critical to successful client matchmaking. We want both humans and dogs to be successful – the temperament evaluations give us an objective method – putting puppies/dogs into three basic categories.
>
> **Category 1 "Make it worth my while"** Puppies or dogs in this group will be assertive, mouthy, and pushy and will need an experienced dog-savvy home. A trainer would be best.
>
> **Category 2: "Whatever you want me to do"** These puppies and dogs accept human leadership naturally. This is the easiest dog to train and to live with. This dog should be successful with children of all ages. This is a low maintenance dog.
>
> **Category 3: "Lions & Tigers & Bears, Oh My!"** Fearful puppies/dogs are either extremely shut down, submissive, or fear biters
>
> Puppies, dogs or adolescent dogs with fear issues are either:
>
> a. Fearfully submissive/shut down and often unresponsive to reinforcement, so they are really difficult to retrain.
>
> b. Fearfully aggressive. Again the fear may be so strong that the dog has no reinforcers that can be used to change their emotional point of view. Sharp/shy dogs are very unpredictable and require 100% management for their whole life.
>
> Some puppies/dogs will not fit neatly into one category. Usually this means the puppy/dog has some good behaviors and some less easy to live with behaviors, which can be modified with smart management and positive training. The categories definitely tell us what kind of home environment and training commitment will be needed for this puppy/dog to be successful (Ganley and Lyon, 2004).

Threat Behavior:

"A threat is everything that may harm, inflict pain or injury to the individual, or decrease its chances of survival" (Abrantes, 2005, p. 32).

Threat Behavior as Part of a Functional System:

> Threat Behavior is unique to each species or sometimes genus: e.g. dogs and wolves threaten similarly, whereas coyotes and foxes differ somewhat.
>
> If the animal is not pressed further, a threat is not followed by an attack, but serves as a warning. Submitting (e.g. a dog rolling on his back or walking away) usually turns off the attack, but also indicates that the submitting animal has lost the encounter (Klinghammer, 1992, p. 5).

Threat Behavioral Examples:

- Agonistic Pucker
- Vocalizations (growl)
- Height Seeking posturing
- Raised Hackles
- Stiff legs
- Ears forward (confident)
- Moving with exaggerated slowness.

Defensive Threat Behaviors:

- Ears laid back
- Tail tucked
- Vocalization (snarl)
- Lips retracted but longer than in offensive threat, and mouth will be partially open.
- Partial roll-over, using facial expressions and feet defensively

Wolf on the right is threatening with agonistic pucker. He conveys emotional conflict with piloerection and raised paw. The wolf on the left display active submission with tail tuck, crouch and piloerection. Piloerection in both wolves is accentuated by the wind.

Wolf on right does an offensive threat using confident posture, piloerections and ears forward. He may be doing an ambivalent paw-lift, but more likely his foot is raised as he moves forward. The wolf on the left does a partial passive submissive roll-over while also using the thrust of his stiff limbs to actively fend off the threatening wolf.

Aussie has slight agonistic pucker and is growling. He is ready to lunge at the Collie, who is moving away.

Wolf is the Grand Teacher. Wolf is the sage, who after many winters upon the sacred path and seeking the ways of wisdom, returns to share new knowledge with the tribe. Wolf is both the radical and the traditional in the same breath. When the Wolf walks by you – you will remember.

– Robert Ghost Wolf

The wolf standing in the background is leaning toward and over the wolf he is threatening with his posture and agonistic pucker. The wolf in the foreground does a dramatic submissive crouch, and paw-lift, He has also lowered his head and tail.

Tongue Flick:

(Also see *Lick Intention, Lip Lick, Distance Increasing Behavior*)

Dogs may lick nose or lips (lip lick) or may simply push his tongue out of the front of his mouth momentarily (tongue flick). This behaviour is likely a remnant behaviour of pushing the mother's nipple out of the mouth when he is sated. Among mammals it is universally recognized as a signal for a moment to think (Sue Alexander, letter to author, October, 2007).

Tongue, Spatulate:

(See *Spatulate Tongue*)

Toss:

(See *Predation* and *Predatory Play*)

In the context of play, the toss, also called the "*kill toss*" is a *redirected behavior*. Some canids in the wild shake and toss small prey animals as a means of killing the animal. They might also toss the dead or dying animal around as a form of play, before or after killing it.

Monty Sloan

Although it looks as though the vole is making a suicidal leap into the wolf's mouth – in fact, the wolf has tossed the vole into the air after having killed it. It will make a small snack.

Turn Away:

(Also see *Displacement Behavior*, *Distance Increasing Behavior*)

The turn away is a *distance increasing behavior*. A turn away may occur when either or both canids are uncertain that they wish to continue an interaction. The turn away may be accompanied by one or several other communication displays.

The dog on the right demonstrates a turn away, and a paw-lift. Note also raised tail and ears that are angled back. He is choosing to turn away rather than continue the interaction. Wicked, the dog on the left, is standing in a confident, heightened posture, with his tail raised high over his back, but he is doing a lip lick, which suggests that he too is uncertain about continuing the interaction.

Turning Backs to Stress:

(See *Cut-Off Signals*)

Umwelt:

Jacob von Uexkull, who wrote *A Stroll Through the World of Animals and Men* 45 years ago, was one of the first people to try to imagine the world as lived and perceived by insects and animals. He created the word Umwelt to describe the world around a living thing as that creature experiences it. It's easy to understand why he had to create a new word, instead of using one that already existed. There is no word in English or German that stands for the world of an animal as that animal experiences it. Words such as "world," "experience," "nature," or "reality," won't do. Umwelt expresses something quite different – it stands for organized experience that is not shared by all creatures, but is special to each creature (Kohl, 2000, p. 5).

Wolves are not our brothers; they are not our subordinates, either. They are another nation, caught up just like us in the complex web of and life.

– Henry Beston

The caribou feeds the wolf, but it is the wolf who keeps the caribou strong.

– Keewation (Inuit) proverb

For the strength of the Pack is in the Wolf, and the strength of thw Wolf is in the Pack.

– Rudyard Kipling

Chorus howl.

Photo by Monty Sloan

Section 25:
Vacuum Behavior − Zoomorphism

Vacuum Behavior:

An activity involving an instinctive, unconscious, or response behavior in the absence of the stimulus that would elicit that behavior. Such activity seemingly has no apparent, contextual, useful purpose (Overall, 2001, p. 3).

Vocalizations:

(Also see *Allelomimetic Behavior, Et-Epimeletic Behavior*)

Canids use various forms of vocalization to express emotion and intent.

- **Baying:** "Certain breeds, such as hounds, have transformed the wolf's howl into a "bay," used to spur other hounds, as well as the hunter, into the chase (Dibra and Crenshaw).

- **Crying, whimpering, whining:** Might convey *fear*, frustration, loneliness, or be an *et-epimeletic behavior* seeking care-giving attention.

- **Rapid-fire repetition** of a single bark, without variation in tone, volume, or posturing conveys "Go Away! Go Away!"

- **Warning or threatening barking:** with variations in tone, volume, and cadence, may be interlaced with growling and huffing, conveying a warning or threat. Warning barks are usually lower in tone and throatier. Note: *commissure* will be short and other threatening postures will be present.

- **Demand barking:** signals frustration and desire to interact or possess. Demand barking may sound shrill, especially compared to warning barks. It is likely to increase in volume and intensity if uninterrupted by distraction or fulfillment of the dog's desire. *Commissure* will be long, lips relaxed, and posture will be bouncy and eager.

Marco De Kloet

The howling sounds produced by hounds known as baying.

Marco De Kloet

Wicked issues a staccato series of frustration or demand barks.

- **Chuffing:** canids puff out their cheeks with air, then rapidly express the air with a "chuffing" sound. It may sound like a muffled bark. It is a vocalization used to greet or warn humans, or other canids.

- **Howling:** When animals compete, they often engage in behaviors designed to exaggerate their size. Wolves stand tall, raise their hackles, ears and tails, and produce low, menacing growls, all to convince their opponent that a retreat from this "big, bad wolf" is the best option. Thus, most confrontations involve a lot of bluff and very little bloodshed. Similarly, packs that are able to exaggerate their numbers are more likely to keep their neighbors at bay. The structure of a pack or chorus howl is well suited to this kind of deception.

Pan is beginning to puff out his cheeks in preparation to chuffing, above and below.

Rather than using howls with a single pure tone, wolves howling in a chorus use wavering or modulated howls. The rapid changes in pitch make it difficult to follow one individual's howls if several others are howling simultaneously. In addition, as the sound travels through the environment, trees, ridges, rock cliffs and valleys reflect and scatter it. As a result, competing packs hear a very complex mix of both direct sound and echoes. If the howls are modulated rapidly enough, two wolves may sound like four or more.... This phenomenon is called the Beau Geste Effect (Harrington, www.pbs.org/wgbh/nova/wolves/howl.html).

Wolves also howl singly to communicate location between established pack members on the move, or at a distance from each other.

Lone wolf howling

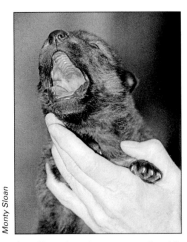

A wolf pup less than two-weeks-old howls.

Wolves are not the only canids that howl. All coyotes howl, for communicative purposes similar to wolves. Some dogs also howl. Depending on the size of the dog their howls may sound just like a wolf's. Smaller dogs' howls will not have the tonal depth of larger dogs and wolves. Many dogs, even small ones, howl as accompaniment to the sounds of fire engine sirens, or train whistles. Sometimes dogs howl as a socially facilitated behavior, because they hear other dogs barking or coyotes howling in the distance.

Howling is generally an adult canine behavior, although wolf pups will sometimes howl. Dogs often don't howl because of their neotonic (life-long, infantile) traits.

- **Huffing** is a vocalization used during *ritualized aggression* and play. The sound is created by air being rapidly expressed over the vocal chords, usually with the canid's mouth wide open, and may be intermingled with growling and other vocal effects.

Whiskers Flared:

Some canids use their whiskers as an eloquent means of communication. They might flare their whiskers forward when they are feeling *agonistic* arousal; or backwards when they feel fearful or submissive. Some people shave dogs' whiskers in the name of grooming. Dogs use their whiskers expressively more than many people realize.

Relaxed fox's whiskers angle back toward his face

Monty Sloan

Two foxes are doing dramatic flared whisker displays.
Photo by Monty Sloan

Monty Sloan

Dog aroused by presence of an unfamiliar dog has flared her whiskers forward.

Barbara Handelman

Whiskers, Lumpy Bed:

The lumpy whisker bed is seen in dogs as well as in their canid cousins described below:

> ... a description of muscle tension in the area of the vibrissae on the wolf's upper lip, on either side of the fleshy portion of the nose. It is a precursor to an agonistic pucker and wrinkling of the nose, with the muscles just beginning to tense when an agonistic pucker is incipient (Goodman, et al., 2002, p. 19).

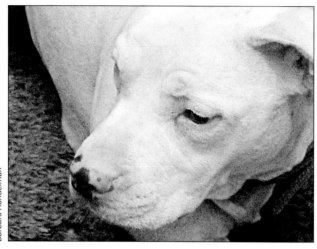

Barbara Handelman

Five-year-old Pit Bull with lumpy whisker bed, just prior to doing an agonistic pucker.

Worried:

Barbara Handelman

Moon, as a puppy, is a portrait of worried expressions. His head is hanging down and his eyes are downcast and his shoulders and back are rounded.

Yawning:

Canids yawn for several reasons. They might yawn as an indicator of stress. They might also yawn to relieve their own physical tension, or because they are uncertain about something they have been asked to do. Of course, they might also yawn simply because they are sleepy puppies.

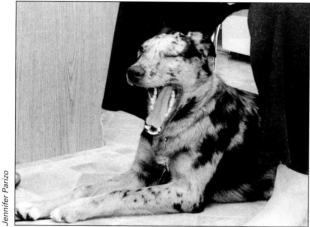

Jennifer Parizo

Stress yawn.

Barbara Handelman

This pup is very stressed, because he has just left his litter.

Barbara Handelman

The coyote puppy on the right is doing a yawn and a paw-lift, both are displacement behaviors. Both pups have their ears turned out to the side which suggests some degree of emotional conflict or uncertainty.

Barbara Handelman

Sleepy puppies yawn too.

Zoomies:

(Also see *Play*)

Zoomies are the flat out joyous-appearing runs that some dogs engage in when stressed.

Young dogs, unaccustomed to the emotionally charged atmosphere at competitions, are apt to blow past agility obstacles or not respond to their handlers' directions in other competition venues.

Handlers and observes alike are prone to seeing zoomies as examples of deliberate disobedience when, in fact, zoomies are indicators of excitement arousal and stress.

In the normal course of a day, puppies are apt to get energy spurts during which they dash exuberantly around the house or yard. This play-run behavior is also known as zoomies.

Zoomorphism:

Zoomorphism is the opposite of *anthropomorphism*, it occurs when animals regard humans as members of their own species. Zoomorphism occurs when animals imprint – attach to a human instead of a member of their own species – at a critical period during their development.

Happiness is a warm puppy.
– Charles Schulz

There is no faith which has never yet been broken, except that of a truly faithful dog.
– Konrad Z. Lorenz

A hungry wolf at all the herd will run. In hopes, through many, to make sure of one.

– William Congreve

Photo sequence: fighting over a pig's ear

I've always said that the best wolf habitat resides in the human heart. You have to leave a little space for them to live.

– Ed Bangs

What is going to happen next? Your guess is as good as mine. This moment might be followed by a play chase. The German Shepherd and the Belgian Tervuren are both mid-flight, but have no apparent aggression in mind – they look entirely playful. The Lab's tail is held high, and his legs are braced, poised for take off, or readying himself to be the landing pad. It could be either.

Photo by Marco De Kloet

Section 26:
Final Quiz – What is Happening?

How many behaviors can you identify in these photos? The answers begin on page 295.

Marco De Kloet

1

Marco De Kloet

2

Sabarika

3

Sabarika

4

Marco De Kloet

5

Marco De Kloet

6

Barbara Handelman

7

Barbara Handelman

8

Monty Sloan

9

Barbara Handelman

10

Monty Sloan

11

Monty Sloan

12

Barbara Handelman

13

Barbara Handelman

14

Monty Sloan

15

Barbara Handelman

16

Barbara Handelman

17

Marco De Kloet

18

Marco De Kloet

19

Marco De Kloet

20

Monty Sloan

21

Monty Sloan

22

23

24

Quiz Answer Key

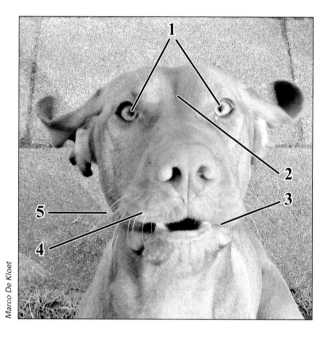

Marco De Kloet

1

This Visla has some known aggression issues. At the moment this picture was taken, he was about to make a grab for the camera, as if it were a ball he could claim for himself.

1. Hard stare

2. Furrow between his eyes – contributes to the hard stare

3. Commissure is forward

4. Lumpy whisker bed – precedes agonistic pucker

5. Whiskers beginning to flare forward

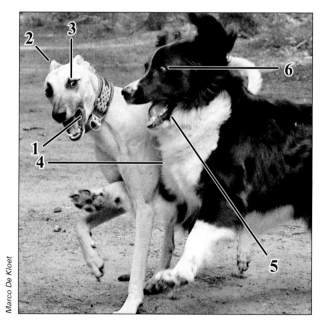

Marco De Kloet

2

Wicked is playing with a familiar dog. Wicked enjoys rough body contact with other dogs. Here he is given a solid body slam. The fact that Wicked's ears are back, his lips are tense, and he's showing whale eye makes it clear that he is not happy with the other dog's action, but this is still a playful interaction.

Wicked

1. Tense Lips

2. Ears Pinned Back

3. Whale Eye

Black and White Dog

4. Body Slam

5. Tense Lips

6. Whale Eye

Sabarika

Sabarika

3 and 4

The young Weimaraner on the right is playing tug with an older dog. The older Lab has a full mouth grip on the toy, while the younger dog holds the toy with only his front teeth and pre-molars. In photo #4, the Weimaraner lies down as a means of *self-handicapping* in order to "level the playing field" and encourage his opponent to continue the game.

Weimaraner

1. Bow posture – invitation to play

2. Toy held in front teeth

Lab

3. Full mouth grip on the toy

4. Ears Forward – relaxed

5. Full mouth grip on toy

Weimaraner

6. Self-handicapping lying down position

7. Self-handicapping front teeth-only grip on toy

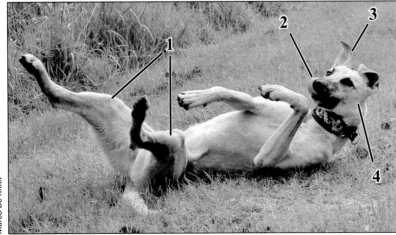

Marco De Kloet

5

Wicked is *rolling,* but not relaxed. He may be trying to keep an eye on other dogs near by. His legs are held stiffly at the joints, and his head is raised. His ears are pitched forward, and he is lip licking, as a displacement signal.

1. Legs stiff at the stifle joint

2. Lip licking

3. Ears forward

4. Head raised

Marco De Kloet

6

Wicked is very relaxed, either rolling for joy, or doing a equally enjoyable *scent roll*.

1. Head Lowered to the ground

2. Front legs are relaxed

3. Hind legs are relaxed

Barbara Handelman

7

Pan is doing a *rude butt sniff*. Ian is turning back to look at Pan, with mild *whale eye* revealing his annoyance.

1. Rude butt sniff

2. Ears pressed back

3. Whale eye

4. Mouth closed and tense

Barbara Handelman

8

Bianca (on the left) and Louie (on the right) have been having one of their rough and tumble play interactions. When Louie gets aroused, Bianca usually responds by biting at his body. It is a game to them, but it teeters on the edge of tipping over into real aggression. In this picture, Pan apparently sensed that they were playing too close to the edge and did a very neat *split*, creating separation between Louie and Bianca.

Bianca

1. Bianca's shoulders and body weight are lowered.

2. She is displaying pinch ear, with her ears flattened against her head one can see a groove down the center created by the pinch.

3. Bianca and Louie are doing a *face off* with direct eye-to-eye contact.

Louie

4. Louie's lips are relaxed, his mouth open and the *commissure* is long.

5. Louie's ears are up and forward.

6. Louie's head is held high as part of his very confident posture.

7. Louie's tail is held fairly high and is wagging.

Pan

8. Pan is executing a *split* so close to Louie that he appears to be passing with shoulder-to-shoulder contact.

9. Pan's ears are in a neutral position

10. Pan's head is lowered, all of Pan's postural cues express his neutrality in this interaction.

Monty Sloan

9

Ruedi, the lowest ranking wolf in the pack, and Woton are engaged in a very tense interaction. Ruedi's displays are *actively submissive* – he is on his side, but his head is raised, and while he offers an *appeasing tongue flick* he is also doing an *agonistic pucker*. Woton's *lateral display* is a serious *threat*, the lines of his body are straight and tense.

Ruedi

1. Hard stare

2. Ears flattened

3. Agonistic pucker

4. Short tense lips with *commissure* forward, mouth closed

5. Appeasing tongue flick

6. Side lying submissive posture

7. Tail tucked

Woton

8. Short tense lips with commissure forward, mouth closed

9. Hard stare

10. Mild *piloerection*

11. Tail above the level of the back

12. Lateral display

13. Ears forward and to the side, connotes tension

Barbara Handelman

10

Lear (on the left) and Bianca (on the right) are playing. Their interaction is full of ritualized *metasignals,* conveying to each other that they are playing. It is interesting to compare the postures and communicative displays in this photo with those in Photo #9. It is as if the dogs are "play acting" what the wolves are portraying with utmost seriousness. There is a third, barely visible, dog in this picture. Louie is lying quietly behind Lear. Louie is so comfortable with the playful interaction between the other two dogs that he has not bothered to move out of the spot where he has settled in the cool shade.

Lear

1. Relaxed waving tail

2. Play bow (shoulder bow) is an important metasignal conveying playful intent

3. Ears relaxed

4. Mouth open, lips relaxed

5. Agonistic pucker

Bianca

6. Soft eyes

7. Lips long and relaxed, mouth open, *commissure* well back

8. Ears are relaxed and a bit forward away from her head

9. Lateral display with soft curving line to her body

10. Tail relaxed and waving

Louie

11. Louie lying contentedly in the shade

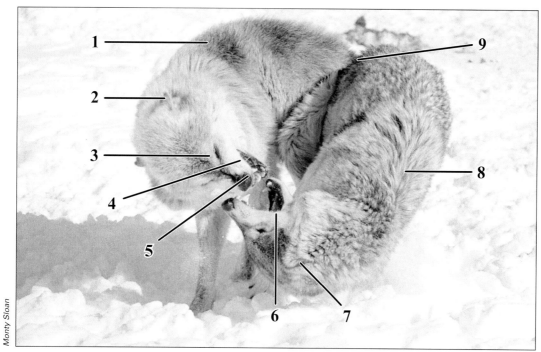

11

Miska (left) and Marion, are two wolves who do not like one another very much. Nevertheless, they have just mated, and are tied. They are also *jaw wrestling* to display their annoyance with each other.

Miska

1. Piloerection
2. Ears plastered back
3. Hard eyes
4. Tense lips, commissure forward
5. Agonistic pucker

Marion

6. Short tense lips, commissure forward
7. Ears plastered back
8. Piloerection
9. Copulatory tie

12

Kailani is muzzle nudge greeting Woton. This type of adult-to-adult canine greeting is considered a *redirected behavior* related to puppies looking to be fed by adults regurgitating food.

1. Soft eyes
2. Muzzle nudge greeting
3. Ears relaxed in neutral position

13

Pan is approaching a potential new friend – Puck the cat. Pan curves his body as he approaches laterally rather than moving in a straight line toward the cat.

1. Quietly waving tail wag

2. Ears forward

3. Curved body, lateral approach

4. Soft eyes

5. Long relaxed lips, mouth open

14

Pan has made a new friend. Puck and Pan do a *head press*, an affectionate greeting.

1. Head press

2. Gently waving tail wag

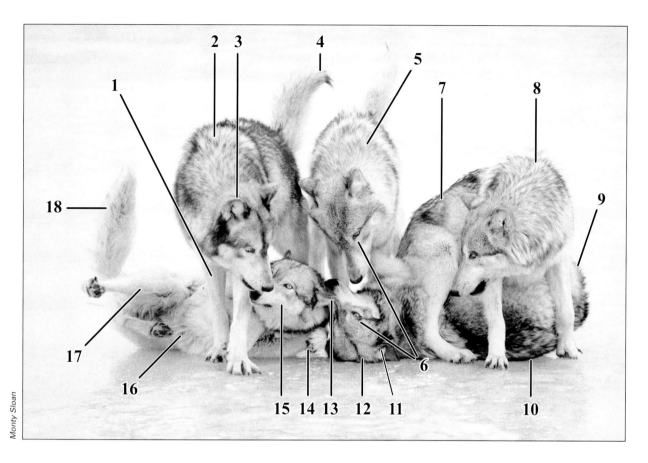

Monty Sloan

15

Tristan, Woton, and Wolfgang, the 1st, 2nd, and 3rd ranking wolves respectively, are *dominating/ standing over* Kailani (female on right) and Renki (male on left).

Tristan

1. *Standing Over* – confident posture
2. *Piloerection*
3. Ears forward – sign of confidence
4. Tail raised – sign of confidence

Woton

5. *Piloerection*
6. Direct eye to eye stare with Kailani

Wolfgang

7. Sitting on Renki – confident posture
8. *Piloerection*

Renki

9. Tail tucked
10. *Passive submissive* roll over
11. Ears pinned back
12. Head lowered to the ice

Kailani – Posture is mixture of *passive and active submissive* positions

13. Ears neutral
14. *Paw-lift* in appeasement
15. Head raised and turned
16. Submissive side-lying with head and hind quarters raised
17. Hind legs poised for action
18. Tail wagging

Barbara Handelman

16

Bianca (on the left), Lear (Bianca's son, in the middle), and Louie are playing. Their play is intense, but there are many *metasignals* that make clear that this is still play, with no agonistic intent.

Bianca

1. Shoulders are lowered, and body posture is relaxed.

2. Inhibited bite to Lear's tail.

3. Tail wagging in a relaxed manner

Lear

4. Lear is either about to do a shoulder bow, or is rolling to his side to lie down in a submissive posture.

5. Dropped, relaxed shoulder

6. Lips are long and relaxed, *commissure* is long

Louie

7. Soft eyes

8. Relaxed body posture

9. Ears relaxed

10. Curving body line

11. Tail waving in a relaxed manner

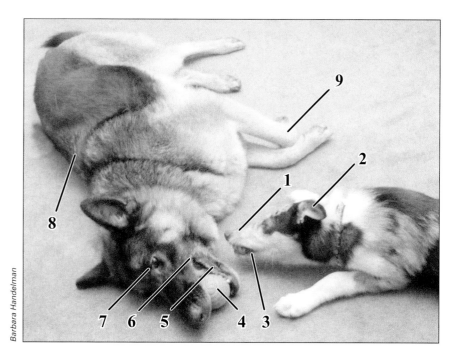

Barbara Handelman

17

Pan is taking advantage of his *puppy license*! He is threatening Luca with an *agonistic pucker*, with his ears plastered back. Luca, for his part, is the very picture of tolerance. He is *self-handicapping* in every possible way – lying on his side, and holding a ball in his mouth.

It is interesting to note that in nearly every photo of Luca and Pan playing (there are hundreds of photos of them) – when Pan was a young puppy – Luca always, by his own choice, has something in his mouth. Luca has a very "hard mouth". Without any intention to inflict harm, he plays roughly, often using his mouth either to issue an inhibited, but nonetheless powerful bite, or a muzzle punch. Having a ball or another toy in his mouth clearly limits the force with which he can use his mouth during these playful interactions. By contrast, when Luca plays with adult dogs, or humans, he employs little impulse control in regard to the strength he exerts with his mouth.

Pan

1. *Agonistic pucker*
2. Ears plastered back
3. Lips are tense, *commissure* is very far forward

Luca

4. *Self-handicapping* by holding a ball in his mouth
5. Long relaxed lips
6. *Commissure* is long (far back)
7. Soft eyes
8. *Self-handicapping* by lying on his side (also a very non-threatening posture)
9. *Appeasing paw-lift* while lying down

Marco De Kloet

18

Three dogs are playing. There is some tension between them, but there are also several indicators that this is still a playful interaction.

Lab, on the right

1. *Paw-over-back*, indicates intention to *ride up* – and possibly mount the German Shepherd mix in the middle.

2. Ears forward with some tension.

3. Lips long, *commissure* well back

4. Foreleg is about to *clasp* the other dog

5. Tail raised, indicating tension

Shepherd X, in the center

6. *Whale eye*

7. *Inhibited foreleg bite*

Belgian Tervuren, on left

8. Long lips

9. Curving body posture with shoulders lowered

10. Ears are neither forward nor back, indicating some degree of emotional uncertainty about the interaction

Marco De Kloet

19

This is a complex interaction between four dogs. All the dynamics cannot be discerned from a single photo. It appears that Wicked (in the center), Anna (brindle dog in the background) and the black and white dog, on the left, were having a fun romp. The small white dog on the right seems to be an intruder, who is trying to *threaten* Wicked. Wicked appears to be switching into avoidance mode in mid-stride.

Small White Dog

1. *Agonistic pucker*

2. *Piloerection*, over the rump

3. Tense lips

Wicked

4. Short tense lips

5. Ears back

6. Body weight to the left in an effort to avoid the small dog.

Black and White Dog

7. *Rocking horse style gait*, indicative of playful intent

8. Carrying a stick is apparently part of the game that was going on moments before

Marco De Kloet

20

The Belgian Tervuren on the left and the Shepherd in the center are playing roughly, with the Shepherd doing a hard *shoulder slam*. The Lab, although not directly involved in the action, is following the action intently.

Terv

1. Ears up and turned to the sides, suggesting tension and ambivalence about the interaction

2. Direct stare

3. *Agonistic pucker*

4. *Inhibited bite* to the neck

Shepherd

5. *Shoulder slam*

6. *Lolling tongue* from open mouth

7. *Whale eye* (eyes turned sharply to return the Terv's stare)

Lab

8. Lips are long, mouth open

9. Eyes watching the action intently

10. Ears forward – alert and ready for action

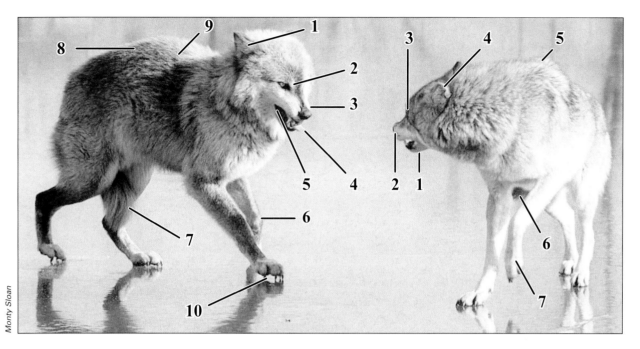

Monty Sloan

21

Engaged in a *face off*, these two wolves are offering a variety of *displacement signals* along with signs of *fear* and distinct *agonistic* threats. They are neither *submissive* nor confident. The observer cannot predict from this frozen moment in time, whether the interaction will escalate or whether one of the two will submit and retreat.

Wolf on the Left:

1. Ears pinned back
2. Direct stare
3. Agonistic pucker
4. Exaggerated tongue flick
5. Tense lips, commissure forward
6. Paw-lift
7. Tail tuck
8. Piloerector reflex
9. Arched back
10. Toenails grip the ice, giving the wolf maximum traction should he choose to make a hasty retreat

Wolf on the Right:

1. Tense lips, commissure forward
2. Agonistic pucker
3. Direct stare
4. Ears pinned back
5. Piloerector reflex
6. Tail lowered
7. Paw-lift

22

    This is an aggressive interaction between rival wolves, Woton (left), and Renki (right). They each exhibit serious, warning, agonistic puckers and defensive leg work. Woton is on the offensive, while Renki appears to be the more defensive of the two in this particular interaction.

Woton
1. Ears erect and facing forward
2. *Piloerection*
3. Hard stare
4. Closed mouth, tense lips, commissure forward
5. *Agonistic pucker*
6. Tail raised
7. Offensive strike with a hind leg

Renki
8. Body angled away in defensive avoidance
9. Piloerection
10. Ears turned back but not flattened
11. Tail tucked
12. Mouth open
13. *Agonistic pucker*
14. Hard Stare
15. Defensive *foreleg strike*

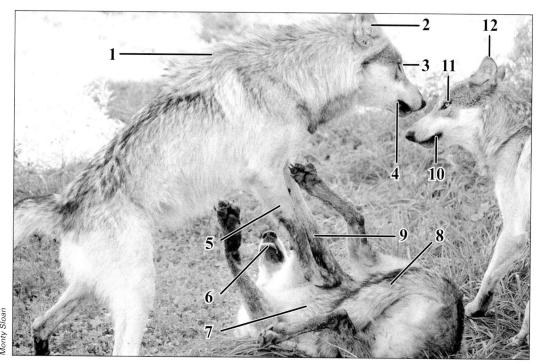

Monty Sloan

23

This is a very tense interaction between three wolves – Woton on the left, Kailani on the right, and Ruedi under Woton. Ruedi is doing his best to *submit to* and *appease* Woton, who is *standing on* him. Kailani and Woton are having a *face off,* threatening each other with direct stares. Woton's posture is most confident – his weight is forward, and directed toward Kailani while he stands on Ruedi. Kailani's weight is directed away from Woton, even while she maintains the *face off* with a direct stare.

Woton

1. *Piloerection*

2. Ears erect turned outward, denotes tension

3. Direct stare at Kailani

4. Very short, tense lips, *commissure* forward, mouth closed

5. *Standing on* Ruedi's chest

Ruedi

6. *Tongue flick – appeasement/displacement behavior*

7. *Passive submissive posture* – lying on back

8. *Tail tucked*

9. Defensive *push off*

Kailani

10. Short, tense lips, commissure short

11. Direct stare at Woton

12. Ears erect turned outward, denotes tension

Monty Sloan

24

Woton (on his back) is *obnoxiously submitting* to Wolfgang, who is beginning to show his annoyance.

Wolfgang

1. *Agonistic pucker*

2. Ears erect and turned out (signifies tension)

3. *Whiskers flared*

4. Tail raised level with back (confidence), *piloerection* apparent in the tail

Woton

5. Ears flattened back

6. *Muzzle nudge*

7. *Pushing off* with hind leg

8. *Submissive roll over*

9. *Tail partially tucked*

*The most affectionate creature
in the world is a wet dog.*

– Ambrose Bierce

*Properly trained, a man
can be dog's best friend.*

– Corey Ford

*Dachshunds are ideal dogs
for small children, as they are
already stretched and pulled
to such a length that the child
cannot do much harm one way
or the other.*

– Robert Benchley

No philosophers so thoroughly comprehend us as dogs and horses.

— *Herman Melville,*
Redburn. His First
Voyage, 1849

When a shepherd goes to kill a wolf, and takes his dog along to see the sport, he should take care to avoid mistakes. The dog has certain relationships to the wolf the shepherd may have forgotten.

— *Robert M. Pirsig,*
Zen and the Art of
Motorcycle Maintenance

A dog teaches a boy fidelity, perseverance, and to turn around three times before lying down.

— *Robert Benchley*

Photography & Design Credits

Douglas Lufkin

Doug created the book layout & cover design, anatomy diagrams and anthropomorphism composite. His company is Lufkin Graphic Designs. To see more of Doug's work, go to: **www.LufkinGraphics.com**

Lynn Crook

Lynn lives in England where she trains and photographs dogs who perform in television, films and other events. To see more of Lynn's work, go to: **www.filmdogs.co.uk**

Marco De Kloet

Marco spends his days with groups of dogs he takes to the beaches and parks of the Netherlands. His camera goes everywhere with him and the dogs in his care. Marco and his dog, Wicked, add both humor and beauty to the book. To see more of Marco's photographs go to: **http://flickr.com/photos/errorsan/** To learn more about his dog walking business, go to **www.blaffenmetgerrit.nl**

Barbara Handelman

Barbara has been a professional photographer for over twenty years. She specializes in photographing dogs, horses, figure skaters and children in action. To see more photographs and video, go to: **www.DogTrainingAtHome.com**

Diane Lewis

Diane is a professional photographer whose images of dogs, horses, and people range from stunning portraits to astounding captures of high speed action. To see more of Diane's work, go to: **www.DianeLewisPhotography.com**

Jennifer Parizo

Jenn is a wonderfully talented amateur photographer. She was my able assistant during many of the dog events where photos for the book were taken. Her contributions of talent, time, and canine behavior awareness are hugely appreciated.

Kevin Peuhkurinen

Kevin is a gifted Canadian photographer who has contributed outstanding images of Sight Hounds enjoying the sport of lure coursing. To see more of Kevin's incredible images of dogs in action, go to: **www.flickr.com/photos/wolfhound/sets/72057594069662674**

Sabarika

Sabarika is an artist who generously makes her excellent photographs of dogs and other animals available to other artists who need models of animal postures and actions. To see more of Sabarika's work, go to: **www.spectralphotoandart.com**

Monty Sloan

Monty's photographs speak of his extraordinary talent far better than words can describe. This book owes much of its depth and power to Monty's photographs of wolves, coyotes, foxes, and dogs. To see more of Monty's work, go to **www.wolfphotography.com** or sign up for Wolf Park Photo of the Day at **www.wolfpark.net**

Giampaolo Urso

Giampi is a highly talented amateur photographer from Bologna, Italy, where he spends time with his dog, Buck, and his camera taking wonderful pictures of dogs interacting at dog parks. To see more of his work, go to **www.flickr.com/photos/cagnacci**

Thank you to:

Bud Crayne, Rachel Friedman, Dee Ganley, Lore I. Haug, Nancy Lyon, Michelle Morgan, Didier Morlot, Marie Ricketts, Dani Kinzel-Waldgeister, and Elizabeth Way for your generous photographic contributions to the book.

Cover and Collage Photo Credits

Front Cover
Clockwise: Monty Sloan, Marco De Kloet, Barbara Handelman, Marco De Kloet

Inside Front Cover
Top to bottom: Marco De Kloet, Marco De Kloet, Monty Sloan

Title Page
Top photo: Sabarika.
Bottom photo: Monty Sloan

Dedication Page
Left to right: Marco De Kloet, Monty Sloan, Marco De Kloet, Monty Sloan, Marco De Kloet, Monty Sloan

Page xiv
All photos by Monty Sloan Page

Page xvii
All photos by Monty Sloan

Page xviii
Clockwise: Marco de Kloet, Marco de Kloet, Marco de Kloet, Marco de Kloet, Barbara Handelman, Barbara Handelman, Marco de Kloet, Barbara Handelman, Dee Ganley, Marco de Kloet, Marco de Kloet

Page 21
Clockwise: Monty Sloan, Monty Sloan, Barbara Handelman, Marco De Kloet, Marco De Kloet, Marco De Kloet

Page 45
Clockwise: Marco De Kloet, Marco De Kloet, Barbara Handelman, Marco De Kloet

Page 59
Clockwise: Marco De Kloet, Marco De Kloet, Barbara Handelman, Barbara Handelman, Marco De Kloet, Marco De Kloet

Page 75
All photos by Marco De Kloet

Page 81
Clockwise: Barbara Handelman, Marco De Kloet, Monty Sloan, Barbara Handelman, Marco De Kloet

Page 95
Clockwise: Barbara Handelman, Marco De Kloet, Barbara Handelman, Marco De Kloet

Page 107
Clockwise: Marco De Kloet, Barbara Handelman, Barbara Handelman, Barbara Handelman, Barbara Handelman

Page 133
Clockwise: Barbara Handelman, Marco De Kloet, Marco De Kloet, Marco De Kloet, Marco De Kloet, Marco De Kloet

Page 149
Marco De Kloet

Page 201
All photos by Marco De Kloet

Page 249
Clockwise: Marco De Kloet, Marco De Kloet, Barbara Handelman, Barbara Handelman, Marco De Kloet

Page 257
Clockwise: Monty Sloan, Monty Sloan, Monty Sloan, Monty Sloan, Barbara Handelman, Monty Sloan

Page 273
All photos by Monty Sloan

Page 280
Clockwise: All photos by Barbara Handelman

Page 313
Clockwise: Marco de Kloet, Marco de Kloet, Marco de Kloet, Monty Sloan

Page 314
All photos by Monty Sloan

Page 318
All Photos by Monty Sloan

Page 323
All Photos by Marco de Kloet

Page 324
Clockwise: Barbara Handelman, Marco de Kloet. Marco de Kloet, Marco de Kloet, Marco de Kloet, Barbara Handelman, Barbara Handelman

Page 331
All photos by Marco de Kloet

Page 332
All photos by Monty Sloan

Page 333
All photos by Monty Sloan

Page 335
Clockwise: Marco de Kloet, Barbara Handelman, Monty Sloan, Barbara Handelman, Marco de Kloet

Page 336
Top photo: Giampaolo Urso.
Bottom photo: Marco de Kloet

page 337
Top and bottom photos: Giampaolo Urso. *Middle photo:* Marco de Kloet

Page 338
Top photo: Marco de Kloet.
Bottom photo: Monty Sloan

Page 339
Top and middle photos: Marco de Kloet. *Bottom photo:* Monty Sloan

Page 340
Marco de Kloet

Page 341
Top photo: Didier Morlot.
Bottom photo: Monty Sloan

Page 342:
All photos by Marco de Kloet

Page 343
All photos by Giampaolo Urso

Page 344
Top photo: Giampaolo Urso.
Bottom photo: Marco de Kloet

Page 345
Top photo: Marco de Kloet.
Bottom photo: Giampaolo Urso

Inside Back Cover
All photos by Marco De Kloet

Back Cover
Clockwise: Monty Sloan, Monty Sloan, Monty Sloan, Marco De Kloet, Marco De Kloet, Marco De Kloet, Monty Sloan, Monty Sloan, Monty, Sloan, Marco De Kloet

Wolves are an essential likeness to ourselves, a mirror in which we can examine ourselves as we can with no other creature. We see in them reflections of our good or evil, our own selfless love and out perplexing violence. We see ourselves as we are and as we might be.

– Peter Steinhart

*Now the hungry lion roars,
And the wolf behowls the moon.*

– Shakespeare
A Midsummer-Night's Dream
v.1.379

Works Cited

Abrantes, Roger. *Dog Language: An Encyclopedia of Dog Behavior*. Naperville: Wakan Tanka, 1997.

The Evolution of Canine Social Behavior. Naperville: Wakan Tanka , 2005.

Alexander, Melissa. *Click for Joy*. Waltham: Sunshine, 2003.

"How You Get Behavior Really Does Matter." *Teaching Dogs. Rpt. in Clicker Solutions*. 2 Sept. 2007 <http://www.clickersolutions.com/articles/2004/gettingbehavior.htm>.

Alexander, Sue. *Aggression Seminar Manual*. Guelph: Dogs in the Park, 2003.

The Quicker Clicker Kit: Dogs in the Park, 2003.

Aloff, Brenda. *Canine Body Language – A Photographic Guide – Interpreting the Native Language of the Domestic Dog*. Wenatchee: DogWise, 2005.

Anderson, Robert K. "Puppy Vaccination and Socialization Should Go Together." *APDT Official Website*. 26 Aug. 2007 <http://www.apdt.com/po/rk_anderson_letter.aspx>.

Appleby, David. "Canine Dominance Revisited." *The Association of Pet Behaviour Counselors*. 2004. 17 June 2007 <http://www.apbc.org.uk/article13.htm>.

"AVSAB Position Statement: The Use of Punishment for Behavior Modification in Animals." *American Veterinary Society of Animal Behavior*. 14 Jan. 2008 <http://www.avsabonline.org/avsabonline/index.php?option=com_content&task=view&id=117&Itemid=302>. Punishment training

Bekoff, Marc. "Do Animals Have Emotions." *The Bark* June 2007: 49-51.

The Emotional Lives of Animals. Novaro: New World Library, 2007.

"Observations of Scent-Marking and Discriminating Self From Others by a Domestic Dog (Canis Familiaris): Tales of Displaced Yellow Snow." *Behavioral Processes* 55 (2001): 75-79.

"Play Signals as Punctuation: The Structure of Social Play in Canids." *Behaviour* 132: 419-429. 10 June 2007 <http://cogprints.org/158/00/199709003.html>.

"Social Play Behavior." *Journal of Consciousness Studies* 8.2 (2001): 81-90. Play

"Wild Justice and Fair Play: Animal Origins of Social Morality." *Program of Dialogue on Science, Ethics, and Religion*. 2003. 17 June 2007 <http://www.aaas.org/spp/dser/02_Events/Lectures/2003/02_Lecture_2003_1016.pdf>.

Bekoff, Marc, and John Alexander Byers. *Animal Play: Evolutionary, Comparative and Ecological Perspectives*. Cambridge: Cambridge University, 1981.

Blakeslee, Sandra. "If You Want to Know if Spot Loves You So, It's in His Tail." *New York Times* 24 Apr. 2007. 10 June 2007 <http://www.nytimes.com/2007/04/24/science/24wag.html?ex=1335067200&en=ab3e625105f41358&ei=5090>.

Blackshaw, Judith. "Notes on Some Topics in Applied Animal Behaviour." *Resources for Applied Ethology*. 2003. 13 Feb. 2008 <http://animalbehaviour.net/AppliedAnimalBehaviourTopics.htm>.

Clothier, Suzanne. *Body Posture & Emotions: Shifting Shapes; Shifting Minds*. Stanton: Flying Dog, 1996.

He Just Wants to Say Hi. 24 Aug. 2007 <http://www.flyingdogpress.com/sayhi.html>.

"College of Veterinary Medicine Pet Health Topics." *Anatomy for the Pet Owner*. U of Washington College of Veterinary Medicine. 16 Jan. 2008 <http://www.vetmed.wsu.edu/ClientED/anatomy/>.

Coppinger, Lorna, and Raymond Coppinger. *Dogs*. 10 June 2007 <http://www.pets.f9.co.uk/shop/media/dogs.htm>.

Coppinger, Raymond, and Lorna Coppinger. *Dogs*. New York: Scribner, 2001.

Coren, Stanley. *How Dogs Think*. New York: Free Press, 2004.

How To Speak Dog. New York: Free Press, 2000.

Craig, Wallace. "Appetites and Aversions as Constituents of Instincts." *Proceedings of the National Academy of Sciences of the United States of America*. 1917. 685-688. 17 June 2007 <http://www.pnas.org/cgi/reprint/3/12/685.pdf>.

Crosby, James W. "Proposed Progressive Dog Bite Assessment (Adapted from Dr. Ian Dunbar)." *Dog Bite Assessment Tool*. 28 Sept. 2008 <http://canineaggression.org/page10.html>.

De Saint-Exupery, Antoine. *The Little Prince*. Trans. Katherine Woods. New York: Harcourt, Inc, 1943.

Dibra, Bash, and Mary Ann Crenshaw. *Dogspeak: How to Learn It, Speak It, and Use It to Have a Happy, Healthy, Well-Behaved Dog*. N.p.: Simon & Shuster, 2001.

"The Myth of the Macho Dog." Online posting. 10 Jan. 1989. *Clicker Solutions*. 10 June 2007 <http://www.clickersolutions.com/articles/2001/macho.htm>.

Dog Reproductive Anatomy and Physiology. 5 Oct. 2007 <http://www.animal.ufl.edu/ANS3317L/badinga/Dog%20reproductive%20anatomy%20and%20physiology.pdf>.

"Dog Socialisation." *The Blue Cross*. 25 Aug. 2007 <http://www.bluecross.org.uk/web/site/Pawprint/AllAboutPets/Socialising.asp>.

Donaldson, Jean. *Fight! A Practical Guide to the Treatment of Dog-Dog Aggression*. San Francisco: Kinship Communications, 2004.

Dunbar, Ian. *Dog Aggression: Biting. 2007*. DVD. Dogwise.com.

"Social Hierarchies." *American Kennel Club Gazette* July 1989. Rpt. in Clicker Solutions. 11 Aug. 2007 <http://www.clickersolutions.com/articles/2001/hierarchies.htm>.

"Social Hierarchies." *Clicker Solutions Training Articles*. 2001. 7 Aug. 2007 <http://www.clickersolutions.com/articles/2001/hierarchies.htm>.

Evans, and Christensen. *Miller's Anatomy of the Dog*. 1964. Philadelphia: W.B. Saunders, 1979.

Fletcher, Thomas. V*eterinary Anatomy at the College of Veterinary Medicine*. U of Minnesota. 16 Jan. 2008 <http://vanat.cvm.umn.edu/>.

Florida Nature. 16 June 2007 <http://www.floridanature.org/>.

Forsythe, Adrien. *The Natural History of Sex*. N.p.: Firefly, 2001.

Fox, Michael W, and Marc Bekoff. "The Behaviour of Dogs." *The Behaviour of Domestic Animals*. 1975. Ed. E.S.E. Hafez. London: Bailliere Tindall, 1975.

Ganley, Dee. *Changing People – Changing Dogs: Positive Solutions for Difficult Dogs*. Glos, UK: Learning About Dogs, 2006.

Ganley, Dee, and Nancy Lyon. "Applying Temperament Evaluation Scoring to Adoption Placement." *Shelter Evaluation Articles*. 15 Oct. 2007 <http://www.deesdogs.com/shelter_evaluations.htm>.

"Glossary." *Primate Info Net*. 6 Jan. 2008 </http://pin.primate.wisc.edu/factsheets/glossary>.

Goddard, M E., and R G Beilharz. "Early prediction of adult behaviour in potential guide dogs." *Applied Animal Behaviour Science* 15 (1984): 247-260.

Goodman, Patricia A., Erich Klinghammer, and Jessica Willard. *Wolf Ethogram*. Ethology Series 3. Battle Ground: Eckhard H. Hess Institute of Ethology, 2002.

Goodwin, Deborah, John W.S. Bradshaw, and Stephen M Wickens. "Paedomorphosis Affects Agonistic Visual Signals of Domestic Dogs." Animal Behavior 53 (1997): 297-304.

Greenberg, Neil. "Ecological Perspective." *Deep Ethology*. 2002. 10 June 2007 <https://notes.utk.edu/bio/greenberg.nsf/854ba168246c6472852563ee006f31ee/74ebb869344f1c69852564a200398829?OpenDocument>.

"Habituation." *Animal Behavior Online*. 18 June 2007 <http://www.animalbehavioronline.com/habituation. html>.

Halfpenny, James C. *Yellowstone Wolves in the Wild*. Helena: Riverbend , 2003.

Handelman, Barbara. "The Marriage of Target and Retrieve." *Dog Training at Home*. 9 Oct. 2007 <http://www. dogtrainingathome.com/targetandretrieve.pdf>.

Hildebrande, Milton. *Analysis of Vertebrate Structure*. 3rd ed. N.p.: John Wiley & Sons, Inc, 1988.

Horwitz, Debra. "Changing the Owner-Pet Relationship." *Atlantic Coast Veterinary Conf.* 2001. 10 June 2007 <http://www.vin.com/VINDBPub/SearchPB/Proceedings/PR05000/PR00470.htm>

The Pet Cast, with Steve Dale. *wgn radio*. wgn. 1 Nov. 2006. Transcript. 10 June 2007 <http://caster. wgnradio.com/podcasts/petpod-013-061101.mp3>.

Introduction to Ethology (The Zoological Study of Animal Behavior). 17 June 2007 <http://cas.bellarmine.edu/ tietjen/ethology/introduction_to_ethology.htm>.

Jensen, Per, Ed. *The Behavioural Biology of Dogs*. Cambridge: CABI, 2007.

John, Holmes. *The Farmer's Dog*. 1960. London: Popular Dogs, 1975.

Johnson, Doug. "A Beginner's Guide to Operant Conditioning." *Clicker Solutions*. 1999. 2 Sept. 2007 <http:// www.clickersolutions.com/articles/2001/ocguide.htm>.

Kalnaijs, Sarah. *The Language of Dogs*. Blue Dog Training & Behavior, 2006. DVD-ROM.

Am I Safe? The Art & Science of Canine Behavior Assessments. 2006. DVD set. Blue Dog Training and Behavior.

Klinghammer, Erich. *Applied Ethology: Some Basic Principles of Ethology and Psychology*. Battle Ground: North American Wildlife Park Foundation, 1992.

Kohl, Judith, and Herbert Kohl. *The View from the Oak*. 1977. New York: The New, 2000.

Lawrence, Ron. "Training Theory." *Doghouse*. 2 Sept. 2007 <http://www.avalanche.org/~doghouse

Lorenz, Konrad. *King Solomon's Ring*. New York: Thomas Crowell, 1952.

Man Meets Dog. Middlesex, UK: Penguin, 1955.

McConnell, Patricia. *For the Love of a Dog – Understanding Emotion in You and Your Best Friend*. New York: Balintine, 2006.

Mech, L David. *The Wolf: The Ecology and Behavior of an Endangered Species*. Minneapolis: U of Minnesota, 1970.

"Alpha Status, Dominance, and Division of Labor in Wolf Packs." *Canadian Journal of Zoology* 77 (May 2000): 1196-1203. 17 June 2007 <http://www.npwrc.usgs.gov/resource/2000/alstat/alstat.htm>.

Merck. "Principles of Behavior Modification and Treatment." *The Merck Veterinary Manual*. 4 July 2007 <http://www.merckvetmanual.com/mvm/index.jsp?cfile=htm/bc/140102.htm>.

Meredith, Michael. *Florida State University Veterinary College*. 23 Oct. 2007 <http://neuro.fsu.edu/~mmered/ index.htm>.

Mirriam-Webster OnLine. 31 July 2007 <http://www.m-w.com/dictionary/pectinate>.

Monks of New Skete. *How to Be Your Dog's Best Friend*. Boston: Little Brown, 2006.

Mullinax, Lisa. "Dog Psychology 101." *4Paws University Dog Training*. 4 July 2007 <http://www.4pawsu. com/dogpsychology.htm>.

Muns, Margaret. "Canine Compulsive Disorders." *Bestfriends*. 24 Aug. 2004. 7 Aug. 2007 <http://network. bestfriends.org/library/download.aspx?d=136>.

Noakes, David. "Animal Behavior Course 2004070." U. of Guelph. Summer-Fall 2004.

"Domestication." Animal Behavior and Zoology Class 4070. University of Guelph. Sept. 2004.

Odendall, J.S.J. "An Ethological Approach to the Problem of Dogs Digging Holes." *Applied Animal Behavior Science* 52 (1996): 200-305. 10 June 2007 <http://www.lapuppyclasses.com/Digging%20Dogs.pdf>.

O'Heare, James. *Aggressive Behavior in Dogs – a Comprehensive Technical Manual for Professionals.* N.p.: DogPsych, 2007.

Overall, Karen. *Clinical Behavioral Medicine for Small Animals.* St. Louis: Mosby, 1997.

"How Animals Perceive the World: Non-Verbal Signaling." *Atlantic Coast Veterinary Conf.* 2001. 10 June 2007 <http://www.vin.com/VINDBPub/SearchPB/Proceedings/PR05000/PR00378.htm>.

"How to Deal with Anxiety and Distress Responses: Dogs." *Atlantic Coast Veterinary Conf.* 2001. 9 Oct. 2007 <http://www.vin.com/VINDBPub/Proceedings/PR05000/PRO00382.htm>.

") Myths and Legends in Animal Behavior: From the Past and Present." *Atlantic Coast Veterinary Conf.* 2001. 10 June 2007 <http://www.vin.com/VINDBPub/SearchPB/Proceedings/PR05000/PR00370.htm>.

Overall, Karen L. "Aggression: Triggers, Flashpoints, and Diagnoses." Paper Presented at *Atlantic Coast Veterinary Conf.* 2001. 14 Jan. 2008 <http://www.vin.com/VINDBPub/SearchPB/Proceedings/PR05000/PR00379.htm>. aggression

Popesko, Peter. *Atlas of Topographical Anatomy of the Domestic Dog.* Vol. 1. Philadelphia: W.B. Saunders, 1975.

Prestwich, Kenneth N. *Evolution and Game Theory.* Course home page. Coll. of the Holy Cross. 19 Sept. 2007 <http://www.holycross.edu/departments/biology/kprestwi/behavior/ESS/ESS_index_frmset.html>.

Price, Edward O. "Behavioral Aspects of Animal Domestication." *The Quarterly Review of Biology* 59.1 (Mar. 1984): 1-32.

Pryor, Karen. *Don't Shoot the Dog.* N.p.: Bantam, 1999.

"The Shape of Shaping: Some Historical Notes." *Karen Pryor's Clicker Training.* 10 Apr. 2007. 2 Sept. 2007 <http://www.clickertraining.com/node/1135>.

Rafe, Stephen. *Command-Train Your Dog to Performance Levels.* Ms. M301. Starfire Products. http://www.starfire-rapport.com/s_index.html.

Ramirez, Ken, Ed. *Animal Training: Successful Animal Management Through Positive Reinforcement.* Chicago: Shedd Aquarium Society, 1999.

Reid, Pamela. *Excel-Erated Learning.* Berkeley: Kenneth and James, 1996.

"Learning in Dogs." *The Behavioural Biology of Dogs.* 2007. Ed. Per Jensen. Cambridge: CABI, 2007. 120-144.

Rogers, Lesley, and Gisela Kaplan. *Spirit of the Wild Dog: The World of Wolves, Coyotes, Foxes, Jackals & Dignoes.* Crows Nest: Australia: Allen & Unwin, 2003.

Rugaas, Turid. *On Talking Terms with Dogs: Calming Signals.* 1997. 2nd ed. Wenatchee: Dogwise, 2006.

Scholz, Martina, and Clarissa Von Reinhardt. *Stress in Dogs.* Wantachee: DogWise, 2007.

Scott, John Paul, and John L. Fuller. *Genetics and the Social Behavior of the Dog: A Classic Study.* 1965. 1974 ed. Chicago: U of Chicago, n.d.

Searle, Edward, Ed. *In Praise of Animals.* Boston: Skinner , 2007.

Segursen, Sheila. "Socialization and Parvovirus Risk." *Shelter Medicine.* UC Davis Shelter Medicine Program. 25 Aug. 2007 <http://www.sheltermedicine.com/documents/ Socialization_and_Parvovirus_Risk.doc>.

"Behavioral Assessment in Animal Shelters." *Maddie's Fund.* 14 Oct. 2007 <http://www.maddiesfund.org/organizations/behavior_assessment.html>.

Seligman, Martin E.P. "Learned Helplessness." *Annual Review of Medicine* 23 (Feb. 1972): 407-412. Play

Serpell, James. *Domestic Dog.* Cambridge, UK: Cambridge University, 1995.

Spector, Morgan. *Clicker Training for Obedience.* Waltham: Sunshine, 1999.

Svartberg, Kenith. "Individual Differences in Behaviour – Dog Personality." *The Behavioural Biology of Dogs.* Ed. Per Jensen. Cambridge: CABI, 2007. 182-206.

The Visual Dictionary. 14 Oct. 2007 <http://www.infovisual.info/02/070_en.html>.

Wells, Virginia. *Structure and Function of the Tail in Dogs*. 24 Aug. 2007 <http://www.petplace.com/article-printer-friendly.aspx?id=4811>.

Wilson, E. O. Interview with Lee Alan Dugatkin. *Principles of Animal Behavior*. By Lee Alan Dugatkin. N.p.: W.W. Norton & Company, 2004.

Wilson, E.O. *Sociobiology: The New Synthesis*. Cambridge: Harvard University, 1980.

Yin, Sophia. "Dominance versus Leadership." *Compendiumvet.com* (July 2007): 415-417.

"Vaccines vs Puppy Socialization: A Confusing Debate?" *Dr. Yin's Behavior Answers*. 25 Aug. 2007 <http://www.nerdbook.com/sophia/article1.html?num=107>.

We are
shaped and
fashioned by
what we love.

– Goethe

The fidelity of a dog is a precious gift,
demanding no less binding moral
responsibilities than the friendship of a
human being. The bond with a true dog is as
lasting as the ties of this earth can ever be.

– Konrad Lorenz

The best place to bury a good dog
is in the heart of his master.

– Ben Hur Lampman

Many who have spent
a lifetime in it can tell
us less of love than
the child that lost a
dog yesterday.

– Thornton Wilder

Topical Bibliography

Aggression

Alexander, Sue. *Aggression Seminar Manual*. Guelph: Dogs in the Park, 2003.

Aloff, Brenda. *Aggression in Dogs, Practical Management, Prevention & Behaviour Modification*. Wanatchee: Dogwise, 2002.

Dunbar, Ian. *Dog Aggression: Biting*. 2007. DVD. Dogwise.com.

Dog Aggression Fighting. 2007. DVD. Dogwise.com.

O'Heare, James. *Aggressive Behavior in Dogs – a Comprehensive Technical Manual for Professionals*. N.p.: DogPsych, 2007.

Anatomy and Physiology

Anatomy for the Pet Owner. U of Washington. 6 Jan. 2008 Anatomy for the Pet Owner. U of Washington. 6 Jan. 2008 <http://www.vetmed.wsu.edu/ClientED/anatomy/#systems>.

Asa, Cheryl S, and Carolina Valdespinot. "Canid Reproductive Biology: an Integration of Proximate Mechanisms and Ultimate Causes." Amer. Zool 38 (1998): 251-259. 5 Oct. 2007 <http://www.icb.oxfordjournals.org/cgi/reprint/38/1/251.pdf >.

Dog Reproductive Anatomy and Physiology. 5 Oct. 2007 <http://www.animal.ufl.edu/ANS3317L/badinga/Dog%20reproductive%20anatomy%20and%20physiology.pdf>.

Evans, and Christensen. *Miller's Anatomy of the Dog*. 1964. Philadelphia: W.B. Saunders, 1979.

Fletcher, Thomas. *Veterinary Anatomy at the College of Veterinary Medicine*. U of Minnesota. 16 Jan. 2008 <http://vanat.cvm.umn.edu/>.

Forsythe, Adrien. *The Natural History of Sex*. N.p.: Firefly, 2001.

Popesko, Peter. *Atlas of Topographical Anatomy of the Domestic Dog*. Vol. 1. Philadelphia: W.B. Saunders, 1975..

Wells, Virginia. *Structure and Function of the Tail in Dogs*. 24 Aug. 2007 <http://www.petplace.com/article-printer-friendly.aspx?id=4811>.

Behavior

Beaver, Bonnie V. *The Veterinarian's Encyclopedia of Animal Behavior*. Ames: Iowa State U, 1994.

The Behavioural Biology of Dogs. Ed. Per Jensen. Cambridge: CABI, 2007.

Fogle, Bruce. *The Dog's Mind: Understanding Your Dog's Behavior*. New York: MacMillan, 1990.

Know Your Dog, an Owners Guide to Dog Behavior. New York: Dorling Kindersley LTD, 1992.

Grandin, Temple and Deesing, Mark J.. "Genetics and the Behavior of Domestic Animals." *Behavioral Genetics and Animal Science*. San Diego: Academic , 1998. 1-53. 17 June 2007 <http://www.grandin.com/references.html>.

Hofmeister, Erik, Melinda Cumming, and Cheryl Dhein. *"Coprophagia In The Canine." Behavior and Training Topics*. Douglas Island Veterinary Service. 2 July 2007 <http://home.gci.net/~divs/behavior/coprophagia.html>.

Horwitz, Debra, and Gary Landsberg. "Compulsive, Stereotypic and Displacement Disorders." *Rutland Veterinary Clinic and Surgical Center*. 7 Aug. 2007 <http://rutlandvet.com/compulsivedisorders.html>.

Merck. "Principles of Behavior Modification and Treatment." *The Merck Veterinary Manual*. 4 July 2007 <http://www.merckvetmanual.com/mvm/index.jsp?cfile=htm/bc/140102.htm>.

Miklosi, Adam, et al. "A Simple Reason for a Big Difference: Wolves Do Not Look Back at Humans, but Dogs Do." *Current Biology* 13 (Apr. 2003): 763-767.

Munn, Margaret. "Canine Compuslive Disorders." *Bestfriends*. 24 Aug. 2004. 7 Aug. 2007 <http://network.bestfriends.org/library/download.aspx?d=136>.

Odendall, J.S.J. "An Ethological Approach to the Problem of Dogs Digging Holes." *Applied Animal Behavior Science* 52 (1996): 200-305. 10 June 2007 <http://www.lapuppyclasses.com/Digging%20Dogs.pdf>.

Overall, Karen. *Clinical Behavioral Medicine for Small Animals*. St. Louis: Mosby, 1997.

"How to Deal with Anxiety and Distress Responses: Dogs." *Atlantic Coast Veterinary Conference*. 2001. 9 Oct. 2007 <http://www.vin.com/VINDBPub/Proceedings/PR05000/PRO00382.htm>.

"Myths and Legends in Animal Behavior: From the Past and Present." *Atlantic Coast Veterinary Conference*. Proc. of ...Atlantic Coast Veterinary Conf 2001. 10 June 2007 <http://www.vin.com/VINDBPub/SearchPB/Proceedings/PR05000/PR00370.htm>

Svartberg, Kenith. "Individual Differences in Behaviour – Dog Personality." *The Behavioural Biology of Dogs*. Ed. Per Jensen. Cambridge: CABI, 2007. 182-206.

Wilson, E. O. Interview with Lee Alan Dugatkin. *Principles of Animal Behavior*. By Lee Alan Dugatkin. N.p.: W.W. Norton & Company, 2004.

Body Language/Communication

Abrantes, Roger. *Dog Language: An Encyclopedia of Dog Behavior.* Naperville: Wakan Tanka, 1997.

Aloff, Brenda. *Canine Body Language – A Photographic Guide – Interpreting the Native Language of the Domestic Dog*. Wenatchee: DogWise, 2005.

Blakeslee, Sandra. "If You Want to Know if Spot Loves You So, It's in His Tail." *New York Times* 24 Apr. 2007. 10 June 2007 <http://www.nytimes.com/2007/04/24/science/24wag.html?ex=1335067200&en=ab3e625105f41358&ei=5090>.

Byrne, Richard W. "Animal Communication: What Makes a Dog Able to Understand Its Master?" *Current Biology* 13: R347-R348. 29 Apr. 2003. 17 June 2007 <http://www.ingentaconnect.com/content/els/09609822/2003/00000013/00000009/art00271>.

Clothier, Suzanne. *Body Posture & Emotions: Shifting Shapes; Shifting Minds*. Stanton, NJ:Flying Dog Press. Stanton: Flying Dog, 1996.

He Just Wants to Say Hi. 24 Aug. 2007 <http://www.flyingdogpress.com/sayhi.html>.

Coren, Stanley. *How To Speak Dog*. New York: Free Press, 2000.

Dibra, Bash, and Mary Ann Crenshaw. *Dogspeak: How to Learn It, Speak It, and Use It to Have a Happy, Healthy, Well-Behaved Dog*. N.p.: Simon & Shuster, 2001.

Goodman, Patricia A., Erich Klinghammer, and Jessica Willard. *Wolf Ethogram*. Ethology Series 3. Battle Ground: Eckhard H. Hess Institute of Ethology, 2002.

Goodwin, Deborah, John W.S. Bradshaw, and Stephen M Wickens. "Paedomorphosis Affects Agonistic Visual Signals of Domestic Dogs." *Animal Behavior* 53 (1997): 297-304.

Kalnaijs, Sarah. *The Language of Dogs*. Blue Dog Training & Behavior, 2006. DVD-ROM.

Milani, Myrna M. *The Body Language and Emotion of Dogs: A Practical Guide to the Physical and Behavioral Displays Owners and Dogs Exchange and How to Use Them to Create a Lasting Bond*. New York: Quill William Morrow, 1986.

Overall, Karen. *Clinical Behavioral Medicine for Small Animals*. St. Louis: Mosby, 1997.

"How Animals Perceive the World: Non-Verbal Signaling." *Atlantic Coast Veterinary Conf.* 2001. Proc. of ...Atlantic Coast Veterinary Conf 2001. 10 June 2007 <http://www.vin.com/VINDBPub/SearchPB/Proceedings/PR05000/PR00378.htm>

Rugaas, Turid. *On Talking Terms with Dogs: Calming Signals*. 1997. 2nd ed. Wenatchee: Dogwise, 2006.

Dogs in Literature

In Praise of Animals. Ed. Edward Searl. Boston: Skinner , 2007.

Paulsen, Gary. *Winterdance: The Fine Madness of Running the Iditarod*. Orlando: Harcourt Brace, 1994.

Domestication

Beach, F., M. Buehler, and I. Dunbar. "Competitive Behavior in Male, Female, and Pseudohermaphroditic Female Dogs." *Journal of Comparative and Physiological Psychology* 96.6 (1982): 885-874.

Frank, Harry, and Martha Gialdinin Frank. "On the Effects of Domestication on Canine Social Development and Behavior." *Applied Animal Behavior* 8 (Aug. 1982): 507-525. Deep Blue at the University of Michigan. 17 June 2007 <http://hdl.handle.net/2027.42/23918>.

Goodwin, Deborah, John W.S. Bradshaw, and Stephen M Wickens. "Paedomorphosis Affects Agonistic Visual Signals of Domestic Dogs." *Animal Behavior* 53 (1997): 297-304.

Price, Edward O. "Behavioral Aspects of Animal Domestication." *The Quarterly Review of Biology* 59.1 (Mar. 1984): 1-32.

Dominance and Leadership

Buitrago, Pamela. "Debunking the Dominance Myth." *Dog Nose News*. Nov. 2004. 18 June 2007 <http://www.clickersolutions.com/articles/2004/Debunking.pdf>.

Appleby, David. "Canine Dominance Revisited." *The Association of Pet Behaviour Counselors*. 2004. 17 June 2007 <http://www.apbc.org.uk/article13.htm>.

Beach, F., M. Buehler, and I. Dunbar. "Competitive Behavior in Male, Female, and Pseudohermaphroditic Female Dogs." *Journal of Comparative and Physiological Psychology* 96.6 (1982): 885-874.

Bekoff, Marc. "Observations of Scent-Marking and Discriminating Self From Others by a Domestic Dog (Canis Familiaris): Tales of Displaced Yellow Snow." *Behavioral Processes* 55 (2001): 75-79.

Buitrago, Pamela. "Debunking the Dominance Myth." *Dog Nose News*. Nov. 2004. 18 June 2007 <http://www.clickersolutions.com/articles/2004/Debunking.pdf>.

Dodman, Nicolas. "The Myth of the Macho Dog." Online posting. 10 Jan. 1989. *Clicker Solutions*. 10 June 2007 <http://www.clickersolutions.com/articles/2001/macho.htm>.

Eaton, Barry. Dominance: Fact or Fiction. Buck: UK: Greenford, 2005.

Horwitz, Debra. "Changing the Owner-Pet Relationship." *Atlantic Coast Veterinary Conf.* 2001. 10 June 2007 <http://www.vin.com/VINDBPub/SearchPB/Proceedings/PR05000/PR00470.htm>

The Pet Cast, with Steve Dale. wgn radio. wgn. 1 Nov. 2006. Transcript. 10 June 2007 <http://caster.wgnradio.com/podcasts/petpod-013-061101.mp3>.

Ryan, Terry. "Assessing the Alpha Roll." *APDT Newsletter* (Aug. 2001): 1+. 17 June 2007 <http://www.apdt.com>. Path: http://www.apdt.com/po/chronicle/article_index.aspx.

"Aversives." *Legacy Canine Training Tips*. 25 Aug. 2007 <http://www.legacycanine.com/tips/aversives_training.html>.

Wilde, Nicole. "Leadership vs. Dominance." *Gentle Guidance 4 Dogs*. 2001. 17 June 2007 <http://www.gentleguidance4dogs.com/dominance_vs_leadership.htm>.

Yin, Sophia. "Dominance versus Leadership." *Compendiumvet.com* (July 2007): 415-417.

Emotions in Animals and The Animal/Human Bond

Bekoff, Marc. "Do Animals Have Emotions." *The Bark* June 2007: 49-51.

The Emotional Lives of Animals. Novaro: New World Library, 2007.

Minding Animals: Awareness, Emotions, and Heart. New York: Oxford University, 2002.

Goodall, Jane, and Marc Bekoff. *The Ten Trusts: What We Must Do to Care for the Animals We Love*. New York: HarperSanFrancisco, 2002.

Masson, Jeffrey Moussaieff. *Dogs Never Lie about Love: Reflections on the Emotional World of Dogs*. New York: Three Rivers, 1997.

McConnell, Patricia. *For the Love of a Dog – Understanding Emotion in You and Your Best Friend*. New York: Balintine, 2006.

Ethology

Abrantes, Roger. *The Evolution of Canine Social Behavior*. Naperville: Wakan Tanka , 2005.

Coppinger, Lorna, and Raymond Coppinger. *Dogs*. 10 June 2007 <http://www.pets.f9.co.uk/shop/media/dogs.htm>.

Coppinger, Raymond, and Lorna Coppinger. *Dogs*. New York: Scribner, 2001.

Coren, Stanley. *How Dogs Think*. New York: Free Press, 2004.

Craig, Wallace. "Appetites and Aversions as Constituents of Instincts." *Proceedings of the National Academy of Sciences of the United States of America*. 1917. 685-688. 17 June 2007 <http://www.pnas.org/cgi/reprint/3/12/685.pdf>.

Dawkins, Richard. *The Selfish Gene*. 1975. Oxford: Oxford University, 1989.

Dodman, Nicholas. " Ethology The Study of Behavior." *Pet Place*. 10 June 2007 <http://www.petplace.com/dogs/ethology-the-study-of-animal-behavior/page1.aspx>.

Fox, Michael W. *Behaviour of Wolves Dogs and Related Canids*. New York: Harper & Row, 1971.

The Dog: Its Domestication and Behavior. New York: Garland STPM, 1978.

Fox, Michael W, and Marc Bekoff. "The Behaviour of Dogs." *The Behaviour of Domestic Animals*. 1975. Ed. E.S.E. Hafez. London: Bailliere Tindall, 1975.

Fox, Michael W., A.M. Blackman, and E. Blackman. "Behaviour and Ecology of a Small Group of Urban Dogs (Canis Familiars)." *Applied Animal Ethology* 1 (1975): 118-127. animalbehavior.net. 10 June 2007 <http://animalbehaviour.net/JudithKBlackshaw/Chapter7b.htm>.

Goodman, Patricia A., Erich Klinghammer, and Jessica Willard. *Wolf Ethogram*. Ethology Series 3. Battle Ground: Eckhard H. Hess Institute of Ethology, 2002.

Greenberg, Neil. "Ecological Perspective." Deep Ethology. 2002. 10 June 2007 <https://notes.utk.edu/bio/greenberg.nsf/854ba168246c6472852563ee006f31ee/74ebb869344f1c69852564a200398829?OpenDocument>.

Introduction to Ethology (The Zoological Study of Animal Behavior). 17 June 2007 <http://cas.bellarmine.edu/tietjen/ethology/introduction_to_ethology.htm>.

Klinghammer, Erich. *Applied Ethology: Some Basic Principles of Ethology and Psychology*. Battle Ground: North American Wildlife Park Foundation, 1992.

Kohl, Judith, and Herbert Kohl. *The View from the Oak*. 1977. New York: The New , 2000.

Lorenz, Konrad. *King Solomon's Ring*. New York: Thomas Crowell, 1952.

Man Meets Dog. Middlesex, UK: Penguin, 1955.

Ridley, Matt. *The Red Queen, Sex and the Evolution of Human Nature*. 1993. NYC: Harper Perennial, 2003.

Scott, John Paul, and John L. Fuller. *Genetics and the Social Behavior of the Dog: A Classic Study*. 1965. 1974 ed. Chicago: U of Chicago, n.d.

Serpell, James. *Domestic Dog*. Cambridge, UK: Cambridge University, 1995.

Learning Theory and Training

Alexander, Melissa. *Click for Joy*. Waltham: Sunshine, 2003.

"How You Get Behavior Really Does Matter." *Teaching Dogs*. Rpt. in Clicker Solutions. 2 Sept. 2007 <http://www.clickersolutions.com/articles/2004/gettingbehavior.htm>.

Alexander, Sue. *The Quicker Clicker Kit: Dogs in the Park*, 2003.

Animal Training: Successful Animal Management Through Positive Reinforcement. Ed. Ken Ramirez. Chicago: Shedd Aquarium Society, 1999.

AVSAB Position Statement: The Use of Punishment for Behavior Modification in Animals." *American Veterinary Society of Animal Behavior.* 14 Jan. 2008 <http://www.avsabonline.org/avsabonline/index. php?option=com_content&task=view&id=117&Itemid=302>. Punishment training

Ganley, Dee. *Changing People – Changing Dogs: Positive Solutions for Difficult Dogs.* Glos, UK: Learning About Dogs, 2006.

"Habituation." *Animal Behavior Online.* 18 June 2007 <http://www.animalbehavioronline.com/habituation. html>.

Handelman, Barbara. "The Marriage of Target and Retrieve." *Dog Training at Home.* 9 Oct. 2007 <http://www. dogtrainingathome.com/targetandretrieve.pdf>.

John, Holmes. *The Farmer's Dog.* 1960. London: Popular Dogs, 1975.

Johnson, Doug. "A Beginner's Guide to Operant Conditioning." *Clicker Solutions.* 1999. 2 Sept. 2007 <http:// www.clickersolutions.com/articles/2001/ocguide.htm>.

Lawrence, Ron. "Training Theory." *Doghouse.* 2 Sept. 2007 <http://www.avalanche.org/~doghouse

Lindsay, S. R. *Handbook of Applied Dog Behavior and Training.* Vol. 1: Adaptation and. N.p.: Iowa State Univ., 2000.

Longton, Tim, and Edward Hart. *The Sheep Dog: Its Work and Training.* North Pomfret: David & Charles, 1976.

Pryor, Karen. *Don't Shoot the Dog.* N.p.: Bantam, 1999.

"The Shape of Shaping: Some Historical Notes." *Karen Pryor's Clicker Training.* 10 Apr. 2007. 2 Sept. 2007 <http://www.clickertraining.com/node/1135>.

Rafe, Stephen. *Command-Train Your Dog to Performance Levels.* Ms. M301. Starfire Products. http://www. starfire-rapport.com/s_index.html.

Reid, Pamela. *Excel-Erated Learning.* Berkeley: Kenneth and James, 1996.

"Learning in Dogs." *The Behavioural Biology of Dogs.* 2007. Ed. Per Jensen. Cambridge: CABI, 2007. 120-144.

Seligman, Martin E.P. "Learned Helplessness." *Annual Review of Medicine* 23 (Feb. 1972): 407-412. Play

Spector, Morgan. *Clicker Training for Obedience.* Waltham: Sunshine, 1999.

Thorpe, W. H. *Learning and Instinct in Animals.* Cambridge: Harvard University, 1963.

Tillman, Peggy. *Clicking with Your Dog.* Waltham: Sunshine, 2000.

Treat, Sally. "Understanding Learned Helplessness." *Journal of the Academy of Canine Behavioral Theory* 1.3 (Fall 2002). 30 Sept. 2007 <http://www.uspcak9.com/training/vol1no3.pdf>.

Yin, Sophia. *How to Behave so Your Dog Behaves.* Neptune City: T.F.H., 2004.

Play

Bekoff, Marc. "Play Signals as Punctuation: The Structure of Social Play in Canids." *Behaviour* 132: 419-429. 10 June 2007 <http://cogprints.org/158/00/199709003.html>.

"Social Play Behavior." *Journal of Consciousness Studies* 8.2 (2001): 81-90. Play

"Wild Justice and Fair Play: Animal Origins of Social Morality." *Program of Dialogue on Science, Ethics, and Religion.* 2003. 17 June 2007 <http://www.aaas.org/spp/dser/02_Events/Lectures/2003/02_ Lecture_2003_1016.pdf>.

Bekoff, Marc, and John Alexander Byers. *Animal Play: Evolutionary, Comparative and Ecological Perspectives.* Cambridge: Cambridge University, 1981.

Dodman, Nicholas, Dr. "How Dogs Play." *PetPlace.com.* 18 June 2007 <http://www.petplace.com/dogs/how-dogs-play/page1.aspx>.

Social Hierarchy

Dunbar, Ian. "Social Hierarchies." *American Kennel Club Gazette* July 1989. Rpt. in Clicker Solutions. 11 Aug. 2007 <http://www.clickersolutions.com/articles/2001/hierarchies.htm>.

Socialization

Anderson, Robert K. "Puppy Vaccination and Socialization Should Go Together." *APDT Official Website*. 26 Aug. 2007 <http://www.apdt.com/po/rk_anderson_letter.aspx>.

"Dog Socialisation." *The Blue Cross*. 25 Aug. 2007 <http://www.bluecross.org.uk/web/site/Pawprint/AllAboutPets/Socialising.asp>.

Segursen, Sheila. "Socialization and Parvovirus Risk." *Shelter Medicine*. UC Davis Shelter Medicine Program. 25 Aug. 2007 <http://www.sheltermedicine.com/documents/ Socialization_and_Parvovirus_Risk.doc>.

Yin, Sophia, "Vaccines vs Puppy Socialization: A Confusing Debate?" *Dr. Yin's Behavior Answers*. 25 Aug. 2007 <http://www.nerdbook.com/sophia/article1.html?num=107>.

Stress

Scholz, Martina, and Clarissa Von Reinhardt. *Stress in Dogs*. Wantachee: DogWise, 2007.

Selye, Hans. *Stress without Distress*. Philadelphia: Lippencott, 1974.

Temperament Evaluation

Ganley, Dee, and Nancy Lyon. "Applying Temperament Evaluation Scoring to Adoption Placement." *Shelter Evaluation Articles*. 15 Oct. 2007 <http://www.deesdogs.com/shelter_evaluations.htm>.

Goddard, M E., and R G Beilharz. "Early prediction of adult behaviour in potential guide dogs." *Applied Animal Behavour Science* 15 (1984): 247-260.

Kalnajs, Sarah. *Am I Safe? The Art & Science of Canine Behavior Assessments*. 2006. DVD set.

Segurson, Sheila. "Behavioral Assessment in Animal Shelters." *Maddie's Fund*. 14 Oct. 2007 <http://www.maddiesfund.org/organizations/behavior_assessment.html>.

Wolves and Other Canids

Barry, Lopez. *Of Wolves and Men*. New York: Charles Scribner's Sons, 1978.

Barry, Scott Ian. *Wolf Empire, An Intimate Portrait of a Species*. Guilford: Lyons, 2007.

Brandenburg, Jim. *Brother Wolf: A Forgotten Promise*. Minicqua: North Wood, 1993.

White Wolf: Living with an Artic Legend. Ed. James S. Thornton. Minoequa: NorthWord, 1988.

Feher-Elston, Catherine. *Wolf Song A Natural and Fabulous History of Wolves*. London: UK: Penguin, 2004.

Fox, Michael W. *Behaviour of Wolves, Dogs, and Related Canids*. New York: Harper & Row, 1971.

Halfpenny, James C. *Yellowstone Wolves in the Wild*. Helena: Riverbend , 2003.

Mech, L David. *The Wolf: The Ecology and Behavior of an Endangered Species*. Minneapolis: U of Minnesota, 1970.

"Alpha Status, Dominance, and Division of Labor in Wolf Packs." *Canadian Journal of Zoology* 77 (May 2000): 1196-1203. 17 June 2007 <http://www.npwrc.usgs.gov/resource/2000/alstat/alstat.htm>.

Rogers, Lesley J., and Gisela Kaplan. *Spirit of the Wild Dog: The World of Wolves, Coyotes, Foxes, Jackals & Dingoes*. Crows Nest: Allen & Unwin, 2003.

Smith, Douglas W, and Gary Ferguson. *Decade of the Wolf: Returning the Wild to Yellowstone*. Guilford: Lyons, 2005.

Steinhart, Peter. *The Company of Wolves*. New York: Vintage, 1995.

Websites

Anatomy for the Pet Owner. U of Washington. 6 Jan. 2008 <http://www.vetmed.wsu.edu/ClientED/anatomy/#systems>.

Asian Protection Network. 10 June 2007 <http://http://www.aapn.org/>.

At Our Hands: A Pictorial of Animal Exploitation. 10 June 2007 <http://www.atourhands.com/home.html>.

Datt, Vicki L, and Thomas F. Fletcher. *Gait Foot-Fall Patterns.* 6 Oct. 2007 <http://vanat.cvm.umn.edu/gaits/index.html#top>.

Dunbar, Ian. *Dog Star Daily.* 2 Feb. 2008 <http://www.dogSTARdaily.com>.

Fletcher, Thomas. *Veterinary Anatomy at the College of Veterinary Medicine.* U of Minnesota. 16 Jan. 2008 <http://vanat.cvm.umn.edu/>.

Florida Nature. 16 June 2007 <http://www.floridanature.org/>.

Ganley, Dee. *Dee Ganley Dog Training Services.* 2 Feb. 2008. <http://www.deesdogs.com/>

Meredith, Michael. *Florida State University Veterinary College.* 23 Oct. 2007 <http://neuro.fsu.edu/~mmered/index.htm>.

The Visual Dictionary. 14 Oct. 2007 <http://www.infovisual.info/02/070_en.html>.

DVDs

Dunbar, Ian. *Dog Aggression: Biting.* 2007. DVD. Dogwise.com.

Dog Aggression Fighting. 2007. DVD. Dogwise.com.

Kalnaijs, Sarah. *The Language of Dogs.* Blue Dog Training & Behavior, 2006. DVD-ROM.

Am I Safe? The Art & Science of Canine Behavior Assessments. 2006. DVD set.

All knowledge, the totality of all questions and answers, is contained in the dog.

– Franz Kafka

An animal's eyes have the power to speak a great language.

– Martin Buber

Only a mountain has lived long enough to listen objectively to the howl of a wolf."

– Aldo Leopold"

We humans fear the beast within the wolf because we do not understand the beast within ourselves.

– Gerald Hausman

We have doomed the Wolf not for what it is, but for what we have deliberately and mistakenly perceived it to be... the mythologized epitome of a savage, ruthless killer... which is, in reality no more than a reflexed image of ourself."

– Farley Mowat

Ours was an empire of sorts

With monarchs and messengers -

Those aspiring on high

And those skimming the depths.

Our mountains were your cities,

Our trees your bastions of tranquilty

Our heavens, your heavens.

All this, and more, within the wolf empire.

— Scott Ian Barry

Author Index

The dog was created especially for children.
He is the god of frolic.

– Henry Ward Beecher

Outside of a dog, a book is man's best friend.
Inside of a dog it's too dark to read.

– Groucho Marx

Index

F

G

Q

R

S

Index to Literary Quotes

The Tail End!

Photo by Monty Sloan

Understanding Canine Behavior: A Ten-Week On-Line Course Taught by Barbara Handelman, M.Ed, CDBC

Purpose:

Students will learn to observe and interpret canine behavior. Their new understanding will help them prevent potentially dangerous dog-to-dog, or dog-to-human interactions.

This course meets for ninety-minutes, once a week for ten weeks. The on-line, live course will be offered four times per year beginning September 2009. It will also be available on-demand.

The live course is presented in "seminar style" with ample opportunity for discussion and Q & A with fellow students and the instructor.

Reading assignments will be from the primary text: *Canine Behavior: A Photo Illustrated Handbook*, with supplemental readings assigned by the instructor. Students will view hundreds of new photos of canine interactions. There will also be many videos of canine behavior for students to view and interpret.

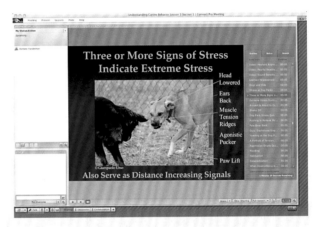

Course Objectives:

As a result of this class, students will:
- Be able to define "behavior" as a concept.
- Become skilled observers of canine behavior.
- Recognize the signs of mild, moderate and severe stress in dogs.
- Recognize different categories of aggressive dog behavior.
- Develop awareness of how anatomy is relevant in understanding and interpreting behavior.
- Recognize and understand:
  - Displacement behaviors
  - Distance increasing behaviors
  - Distance decreasing behaviors
  - Dominance: definition and relevance in behavior
  - Epimeletic and et-epmiletic behaviors
  - Metasignals
- Differentiate different types of canine play.
- Understand predation in domestic canines.
- Understand social hierarchies as they apply to wild and domestic canines.
- Understand the difference between socializing and socialization.

*For more information or to register, go to **www.e-trainingfordogs.com***